THE PIPE FITTER'S AND PIPE WELDER'S HANDBOOK

(Revised Edition)

THOMAS W. FRANKLAND

Formerly Instructor, Steamfitting Department
Washburne Trade School, Chicago, Illinois
Member of Pipe Fitters Association, Local Union 597 U. A.
Chicago, Illinois

Glencoe McGraw-Hill

New York, New York   Columbus, Ohio   Woodland Hills, California   Peoria, Illinois

PREFACE

The author of "The Pipe Fitter's and Pipe Welder's Handbook," through many years of experience in pipe fitting and teaching apprentices in the trade, has gathered basic information which will enable the pipe fitter to solve the difficult problems encountered in this work.

The data which the author has compiled are made available in handy reference form. The manual has been made small enough for the pipe fitter to carry around in a pocket so that it may be consulted whenever he or she is in need of it.

Glencoe/McGraw-Hill

A Division of The McGraw·Hill Companies

Send all inquires to:
Glencoe/McGraw-Hill
4400 Easton Commons
Columbus, OH 43219

ISBN 0-02-802500-8

Printed in the United States
43 44 45 CTM 23

CONTENTS

1

BASIC TRADE MATHEMATICS

METHODS FOR CHECKING ARITHMETICAL PROBLEMS

Method for Checking Multiplication

Example:

```
7654 = 22 =  4
x621 =  9 = x9
                  ——
  7654        36 = 3 + 6 = 9
 15308
 45924
————————
4753134 = 27 = 2 + 7 = 9
```

Explanation:

1. Add the top row of figures until a single number is obtained. Proceed as follows: $7 + 6 + 5 + 4 = 22$; $2 + 2 = 4$.

2. Add the second row of figures: $6 + 2 + 1 = 9$.

3. Multiply these two numbers and reduce their product to a single number: $9 \times 4 = 36$; $3 + 6 = 9$.

Note: The answer of the problem should total 9 or it is wrong.

4. Total the answer: $4 + 7 + 5 + 3 + 1 + 3 + 4 = 27$; $2 + 7 = 9$.

Note: Since the single numbers obtained in steps 3 and 4 are the same, the answer is correct.

Method for Checking Addition

Example:

```
76543 = 25              2 + 5 = 7
96855 = 33              3 + 3 = 6
63961 = 25              2 + 5 = 7
73871 = 26              2 + 6 = 8
56363 = 23              2 + 3 = 5
————————                ————————
367593 = 33 = 3 + 3 = 6     33 = 3 + 3 = 6
```

Explanation:

1. Add the numbers in each horizontal row and reduce their sum to a single number.

2. As shown in the example, add the single numbers thus obtained and reduce their sum to a single number.

3. Total the numbers in the answer and reduce their sum to a single number.

Note: If the single numbers obtained in steps 2 and 3 are the same, the answer is correct; if not, it is incorrect.

Method for Checking Division
Example:

```
      5.091 =15= 6      356.431
70 | 356.431   70=x7       — 61
      350      ——————    ——————
      ———      42=6      356.370 =24=2+4= 6
      643
      630
      ———
      131
       70
      ———
       61 (Remainder)
```

1. Total the answer, and reduce the sum found to a single number: $5 + 0 + 9 + 1 = 15$; $1 + 5 = 6$.

2. Total the divisor, and reduce the sum found to a single number: $7 + 0 = 7$.

3. Multiply the two single numbers thus obtained, and reduce their product to a single number: $6 \times 7 = 42$; $4 + 2 = 6$.

4. Subtract the remainder, if there is one, from the dividend; then total the answer: $3 + 5 + 6 + 3 + 7 + 0 = 24$; $2 + 4 = 6$.

Note: If the single numbers obtained in steps 3 and 4 are the same, the answer is correct.

SQUARE ROOT OR SQUARE OF A NUMBER

The square root of a particular number is another number which when multiplied by itself equals that particular number. For example, the square root of 49 is 7, since $7 \times 7 = 49$.

Solutions to pipe layout problems involve basic math such as multiplying, dividing, adding, and subtracting. Some problems require finding square roots of numbers and trigonometric functions of angles.

Much of the work of manual calculations can be done on a hand held calculator. The most simple and inexpensive ones usually include a square root key which simplifies right triangle calculation. Also available are low cost "scientific calculators" which give trigonometric functions at the touch of a key.

Tables in this handbook provide squares, cubes, and square and cube roots.

When using a calculator to find the square of a number simply multiply the number by itself; $15 \times 15 = 225$. Press the calculator keys in order

| 1 | 5 | x | 1 | 5 | = | **225**

As each numbered key is pressed the number appears in the window. The x and = signs do not appear.

To find the square root of a number ($\sqrt{225}$) enter the number by pressing each key in order

| 2 | 2 | 5 | to display **225.** Then press $\sqrt{x}$ and the display will change to **15** which is the square root of **225.**

In solving the example problem for Fig. 1 on page 7, you can manually multiply 15 x 15 and 20 x 20, use the tables in this handbook, or use a calculator.

With a calculator, press the keys in order

| 1 | | 5 | | x | | 1 | | 5 | | = | **225**

Note answer - then press clear key

| CE/C | .

With the display clear, proceed to square the number 20.

| 2 | | 0 | | x | | 2 | | 0 | | = | **400**

With **400** showing in display, add the

400 | + | | 2 | | 2 | | 5 | | = | **625**

Then press √x key which will change the display to **25** which is the length of side C.

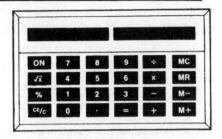

Calculator with √x key

TRIGONOMETRIC FUNCTIONS

Calculators with trigonometric functions (the same values listed in the trigonometry tables in this handbook) have extra keys marked

| arc | | sin | | cos | | tan |

Note that there are no keys for cosecant, secant, and cotangent. These values may be obtained with an extra calculation step from the following relationship formulas.

$$\text{Cosecant} = \frac{1}{\text{Sine}}$$

$$\text{Secant} = \frac{1}{\text{Cosine}}$$

$$\text{Cotangent} = \frac{1}{\text{Tangent}}$$

As an example, if you need to know the secant of an angle, such as $22\frac{1}{2}°$, first find the cosine.

Press keys

$$\boxed{2}\ \boxed{2}\ \boxed{.}\ \boxed{5}\ ,$$

then press key $\boxed{\text{COS}}$. The figure **.9238795326** will appear in the display. (You don't need more than four places – call it .9239). Use the formula

$$\text{Secant} = \frac{1}{\text{Cosine}} = \frac{1}{.9239} = 1.08$$

If you know the sine, cosine, or tangent of an angle you can find the angle by using the key marked $\boxed{\text{arc}}$.

For example, if you know that the cosine of an angle is .9239 but don't know the angle enter **.9239** into the display of the calculator, then press $\boxed{\text{arc}}$ then $\boxed{\text{COS}}$. The display will change to

22.49693537

which is very close to $22.5°$ or $22\frac{1}{2}°$.

The reason the answer was not exactly **22.5** is because only four digits of the value of the cosine were used.

Instruction manuals that come with each calculator can provide other uses.

Solving Right Triangles with Square Root

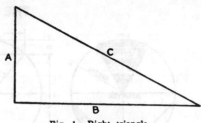

Fig. 1. Right triangle.

Formulas:

$$A = \sqrt{C^2 - B^2}$$
$$B = \sqrt{C^2 - A^2}$$
$$C = \sqrt{A^2 + B^2}$$

The sign $\sqrt{}$ indicates that the square root of the quantity must be extracted. (See the explanation of the method of extracting square root, pp. 4-6.)

Example:

Find the length of C, when A is 15 in. and B is 20 in.

$$C = \sqrt{A^2 + B^2} = \sqrt{15^2 + 20^2} = \sqrt{(15 \times 15) + (20 \times 20)} = \sqrt{225 + 400} = \sqrt{625} = 25 \text{ in.}$$

THE CIRCLE

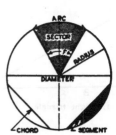

Fig. 2. Parts of a circle.

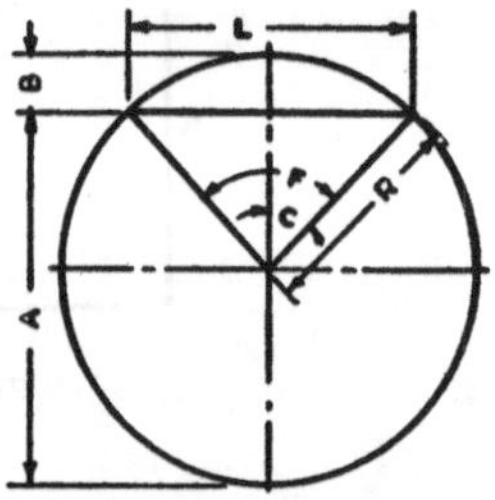

Fig. 3. Parts of a circle (cont'd).

Fig. 4. Parts of a circle (cont'd).

To find the circumference of a circle, multiply the diameter by 3.1416.

The radius of a circle is one-half of the diameter.

An arc is a part of the circumference. To find the length of an arc, multiply the number of degrees in the arc by the radius times .01745.

$$\text{Sine of angle } C = \frac{L}{2} \div R \quad \text{(See Fig. 3.)}$$

$$\text{Angle } F = 2 \times \text{angle } C$$

A chord is a line connecting the ends of an arc. To find the length of a chord, use the following formula:

$$L = 2 \times \sqrt{A \times B},$$

where *L* is the length of the chord and *A* and *B* are the dimensions shown in Fig. 3.

To find the area of a circle, multiply the square of the diameter by .7854.

To find the area of a sector, multiply one-half of the length of the arc by the radius of the circle.

A segment is an area bounded by an arc and a chord. To find the area of the segment *X* shown in Fig. 4:

1. Find the area of the entire sector.

2. Find the area of triangle *Y*. (See p. 174.)

3. Subtract the area of the triangle from that of the sector.

SOLUTION OF RIGHT TRIANGLES WITH TRIGONOMETRY

All piping offsets are based on right triangles. The trigonometry in this section deals with the solution of problems involving right triangles.

Functions of Angles

In computing piping offsets with trigonometry, the tradesman will employ the six functions (technically called trigonometric functions, or ratios) of the angle of fitting. These functions are:

$$\text{Sine} = \frac{\text{set *}}{\text{travel}}$$

$$\text{Cosine} = \frac{\text{run}}{\text{travel}}$$

$$\text{Tangent} = \frac{\text{set}}{\text{run}}$$

$$\text{Cotangent} = \frac{\text{run}}{\text{set}}$$

$$\text{Secant} = \frac{\text{travel}}{\text{run}}$$

$$\text{Cosecant} = \frac{\text{travel}}{\text{set}}$$

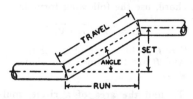

Fig. 5. Piping offset.

The angles equivalent to the sines, cosines, etc., figured out according to the foregoing formulas are found in the Trigonometry Table, pages 190 to 194.

---

*This equation means that the sine of the angle of fitting equals set divided by the travel.

Finding Set, Run, and Travel

Formulas:

Set = travel x sine of angle of fitting, also
run x tangent of angle of fitting

Run = travel x cosine of angle of fitting, also
set x cotangent of angle of fitting

Travel = set x cosecant of angle of fitting, also
run x secant of angle of fitting

Example:

What is the length of run and travel for a 45° offset with a set of 15 in.?

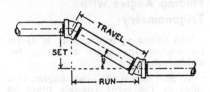

Fig. 6. Piping offset.

Run = set x cotangent of angle of fitting

Run = 15 x 1.000 = 15 in. (length of run center to center)

Travel = set x cosecant of angle of fitting

Travel = 15 x 1.414 = 21.21 in. (length of travel piece center to center)

Finding Angles with Trigonometry

The following information is useful for finding the angle of fitting for welded offsets.

To find one of the acute angles, two sides of the right triangle must be known.

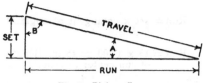

Fig. 7. Piping offset.

Type 1: When the set and run are known, the angle of fitting, *A*, is found by determining the tangent of the angle and obtaining the angle from the Trigonometry Table, p. 190 ff.

Example:

When the set is 18 in. and the run is 24 in., what is the angle of fitting for a welded offset?

$$\text{Tangent of angle of fitting} = \frac{\text{set}}{\text{run}}$$

$$\text{Tangent of angle of fitting} = \frac{18}{24} = .75000$$

$$\text{Angle of fitting} = 37°*$$

---

*See the Trigonometry Table. Tangent .75000 is not shown in the Trigonometry Table. Hence, the number closest to it is used, which is .75355. The angle for this tangent is 37°.

Type 2: When the travel and run are known, angle A is found by determining its cosine and obtaining the angle from the Trigonometry Table.

Example:

When the run is 24 in. and the travel is 30 in., what is the size of angle A?

$$\text{Cosine of angle A} = \frac{\text{run}}{\text{travel}}$$

$$\text{Cosine of angle A} = \frac{24}{30} = .80000$$

$$\text{Angle A} = 37°*$$

---

*See the Trigonometry Table. Cosine .80000 is not shown in the Trigonometry Table. Hence the closest number to it, namely .79863, is used. The angle for this cosine is 37°.

Type 3: When the set and travel are known, angle A is found by determining its sine and obtaining the angle from the Trigonometry Table.

Example:

When the set is 18 in. and the travel is 30 in., what is angle A?

$$\text{Sine of angle A} = \frac{\text{set}}{\text{travel}}$$

$$\text{Sine of angle A} = \frac{18}{30} = .60000$$

$$\text{Angle A} = 37°*$$

Note: To find angle B, subtract angle A from 90°.

---

*See the Trigonometry Table. Sine .60000 is not shown in the Trigonometry Table. Hence the closest number to it, namely .60181, is used. The angle for this sine is 37°.

PIPE BENDS

Simple Bends

Formula:

$L = R \times D \times .01745$

In the formula, *L* is the length of the bend, *R* is the radius of the bend, and *D* is the number of degrees of the bend. If the length of the entire pipe is desired, the length of the tangents must be added to the length of the bend. The symbol of tangent is *T*.

Example:

Find the length of a piece of pipe for a 90° bend with a radius of 40 in. and with two 15-in. tangents.

$L = R \times D \times .01745$

Length of bend = 40 x 90 x .01745 =
$\qquad$ 62.82 in.

Length of pipe = $L + 2T$ = 62.82 + 30
$\qquad$ = 92.82 in. or 7 ft. 8$\frac{13}{16}$
$\qquad$ in. end to end

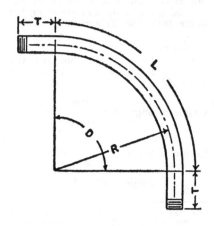

Fig. 8. Simple pipe bend.

Wrinkle Bends

Each wrinkle may vary from 5° to 15° depending on the number of wrinkles required. To determine the length of pipe required for a wrinkle bend, use the following formulas:

Formulas:

Length of bend = degrees of bend x outside radius x .01745

Number of wrinkles = $\dfrac{\text{degrees of bend}}{\text{degrees per wrinkle}}$

Wrinkle spacing = $\dfrac{\text{length of bend}}{\text{number of wrinkles}}$

Example:

What is the length of pipe required to fabricate a 90° wrinkle bend, with an outside radius of 3 ft. 7 in., using 10° wrinkles, with two 10-in. tangents?

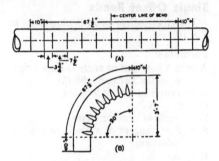

Fig. 9. Wrinkle bend.

Applying the above formulas:

Length of bend = 90 x 43 x .01745 = 67½ in.
Number of wrinkles = 90 ÷ 10 = 9
Wrinkle spacing = 67.5 ÷ 9 = 7½ in.
Total pipe length = 67.5 + 20 = 87.5

Single Offset Bends

The single offset bend is illustrated in Fig. 10.

Formulas:

A = S x cosecant of angle D (See Trigonometry Table, p. 190 ff.)

B = center to face of long leg

C = B — K

D = angle of bend or offset

$S \div F$ = tangent of angle D (if angle is unknown)

E = A — K

F = center to face of short leg

F = S x cotangent of angle D (if angle is unknown)

K = R x tangent of angle P (See Trigonometry Table.)

L = R x D x .01745

P = D ÷ 2

R = radius of bend

S = offset

T = E + L + C = (length of pipe required)

Example:

Find the length of pipe required for a 30° single offset pipe bend, when S = 36 in., B = 60 in. F = 62⅜ in., and R = 36 in.

A = 36 x 2.000 = 72 in. (cosecant 30° = 2.000 from Trigonometry Table)

B = 60 in.

C = 60 — 9⅝ = 50⅜ in.

D = 30°

E = 72 — 9⅝ = 62⅜ in.

F = 62⅜ in.

K = 36 x .26795 = 9⅝ in.
(tangent 15° = .26795 from Trigonometry Table.)

L = 36 x 30° x .01745 = 18²⁷/₃₂ in.

P = 30° ÷ 2 = 15

R = 36 in.

S = 36 in.

T = 62⅜ + 18²⁷/₃₂ + 50⅜ in. = 131¹⁹/₃₂ in. or 10 ft. 11¹⁹/₃₂ in.

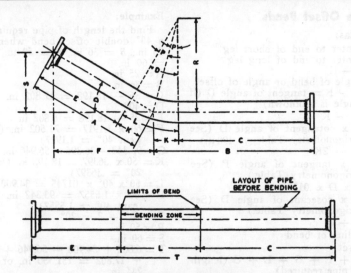

Fig. 10. Single offset bend.

Double Offset Bends

Formulas:

A = center to end of short leg
B = center to end of long leg
C = B — K
D = angle of bend or angle of offset
D = S ÷ F = tangent of angle D (if angle is unknown)
E = A — K
F = S x cotangent of angle D (See Trigonometry Table, p. 190 ff.)
G = M — 2K
K = R x tangent of angle P (See Trigonometry Table.)
L = R x D x .01745
M = S x cosecant of angle D (See Trigonometry Table.)
P = D ÷ 2
R = radius of bend
S = offset
T = E + L + G + L + C (length of pipe required)

Example:

Find the length of pipe required for a 40° double offset bend when A = 25 in., B = 36 in., R = 50 in., and S = 60 in.

A = 25 in.
B = 36 in.
C = 36 — 18.198 = 17.802 in.
D = 40°
E = 25 — 18.198 = 6.802 in.
F = 60 x 1.1917 = 71.502 in. (cotangent 40° = 1.1917)
G = 93.342 — 36.396 = 56.946 in.
K = 50 x .36397 = 18.198 in. (tangent 20° = .36397)
L = 50 x 40° x .01745 = 34.900 in.
M = 60 x 1.5557 = 93.342 in. (cosecant 40° = 1.5557)
P = 40° ÷ 2 = 20°
R = 50 in.
S = 60 in.
T = 6.802 + 34.900 + 56.946 + 34.900 + 17.802 = 151.350 in. or 12 ft. 7⅜ in.

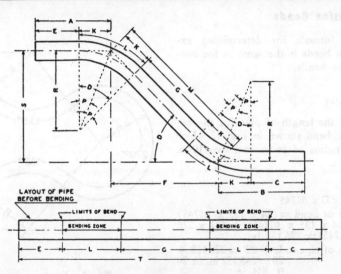

LAYOUT OF PIPE
BEFORE BENDING

Fig. 11. Double offset bend.

Expansion Bends

The formula for determining expansion bends is the same as for simple pipe bends.

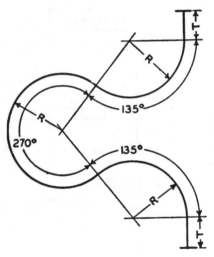

Example:

Find the length of pipe for the expansion bend shown in Fig. 12 which has a radius of 24 in. and two 10-in. tangents.

$L = R \times D \times .01745$

Length of bend $= (24 \times 135 \times .01745)$ $+ (24 \times 135 \times .01745) + (24 \times 270 \times .01745) = 226.152$ in.

Length of pipe $= L + 2T = 226.152 + 20 = 246.152$ in. or 20 ft. 6⅛ in.

Fig. 12. Expansion bend.

LINEAR EXPANSION OF PIPING

Formula:

E = expansion in inches per 100 ft. of pipe

F = starting temperature

T = final temperature

E = constant x (T — F)

CONSTANTS PER 100 FT.

Metal	Constant
Steel	.00804
Wrought Iron	.00816
Cast iron	.00780
Copper and brass	.01140

Example:

What is the expansion of a 365-ft. steel steam line at 75 pounds pressure if the starting temperature is 60° Fahrenheit?

E = constant x (T — F)

Constant = .00804 (See accompanying table.)

T = 320° (See table on p. 164 for boiling point of water at 75 pounds pressure.)

E = .00804 x (320 — 60) = .00804 x 260 = 2.09 in.

Expansion for 365-ft. line = 2.09 x 3.65 = 7.628 in.

CAPACITIES OF TANKS

Rectangular Tanks

Formulas:
C = capacity in gallons; L = length;
W = width; H = height.

When measurements are in inches:

$$C = \frac{L \times W \times H}{231*}$$

When measurements are in feet:
C = L x W x H x 7.48†

Example:
How many gallons of oil will a rectangular tank hold that is 96 in. long, 24 in. wide, and 12 in. high?

$$C = \frac{L \times W \times H}{231}$$

$$C = \frac{96 \times 24 \times 12}{231} = 119\frac{3}{4} \text{ gallons}$$

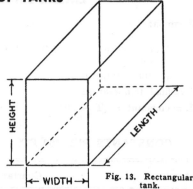

Fig. 13. Rectangular tank.

Example:
How many gallons of water will a rectangular tank hold which is 10 ft. long, 3 ft. wide, and 5 ft. high?
C = L x W x H x 7.48
C = 10 x 3 x 5 x 7.48 = 1122 gallons

---
*Cubic inches in one gallon.
†Gallons per cubic foot.

Cylindrical Tanks

Formulas:

C = capacity in gallons
D = diameter
L = length

When measurements are in inches:

$$C = \frac{D \times D \times .7854 \times L}{231}$$

When measurements are in feet:

C = D x D x .7854 x L x 7.48

Example:

How many gallons of water will a tank hold which is 3 ft. in diameter and 12 ft. long?

C = D x D x .7854 x L x 7.48
C = 3 x 3 x .7854 x 12 x 7.48 = 634.477
or 634½ gallons

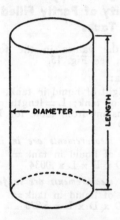

Fig. 14. Cylindrical tank.

Figuring the Approximate Capacity of Partly Filled Round Tanks

For the values in the following formula, see Fig. 15.

Formula:

A = height of liquid in tank; D = diameter of tank; L = length of tank; P = constant from table for K; K = A ÷ D

When measurements are in inches:
Gallons of liquid in tank =
   P x D x D x L x .0034

When measurements are in feet:
Gallons of liquid in tank =
   P x D x D x L x 5.875

Example:

Find the number of gallons of water in a round horizontal tank that is

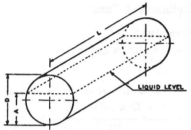

Fig. 15. Partially filled round tank.

4 ft. in diameter and 10 ft. long, containing water that is 2 ft. 9 in. high.

A = 2 ft. 9 in.
D = 4 ft.
L = 10 ft.
K = 2.75 ft. ÷ 4.00 ft. = .687 or .69
P = .7360 (from the accompanying table for K = .69)
Gallons of water = .7360 x 4 x 4 x 10 x 5.875 = 691.840 gallons

Factors for Figuring the Number of Gallons in Round Tanks

K	P	K	P	K	P
.02	.0048	.35	.3118	.68	.7243
.03	.0087	.36	.3241	.69	.7360
.04	.0134	.37	.3363	.70	.7477
.05	.0187	.38	.3486	.71	.7595
.06	.0244	.39	.3610	.72	.7709
.07	.0308	.40	.3735	.73	.7822
.08	.0375	.41	.3860	.74	.7934
.09	.0446	.42	.3988	.75	.8046
.10	.0520	.43	.4111	.76	.8155
.11	.0598	.44	.4237	.77	.8263
.12	.0680	.45	.4364	.78	.8370
.13	.0764	.46	.4490	.79	.8474
.14	.0850	.47	.4617	.80	.8577
.15	.0940	.48	.4744	.81	.8677
.16	.1032	.49	.4872	.82	.8776
.17	.1126	.50	.5000	.83	.8874
.18	.1224	.51	.5128	.84	.8968
.19	.1328	.52	.5256	.85	.9060
.20	.1423	.53	.5383	.86	.9150
.21	.1528	.54	.5510	.87	.9236
.22	.1630	.55	.5636	.88	.9320
.23	.1737	.56	.5763	.89	.9402
.24	.1845	.57	.5889	.90	.9480
.25	.1954	.58	.6012	.91	.9556
.26	.2066	.59	.6140	.92	.9625
.27	.2178	.60	.6265	.93	.9692
.28	.2291	.61	.6390	.94	.9761
.29	.2405	.62	.6514	.95	.9813
.30	.2523	.63	.6637	.96	.9866
.31	.2640	.64	.6759	.97	.9913
.32	.2757	.65	.6882	.98	.9952
.33	.2876	.66	.7003	.99	.9983
.34	.2997	.67	.7124	1.00	1.0000

Elliptical Tanks

Formulas:

C = capacity in gallons; L = length; W = width; H = height.

When measurements are in inches:

$$C = \frac{(W \times H \times .7854) \times L}{231}$$

When measurements are in feet:

$$C = (W \times H \times .7854) \times L \times 7.48$$

Example:

How many gallons of water will an elliptical tank hold which is 120 in. long, 36 in. wide, and 24 in. high?

$$C = \frac{(W \times H \times .7854) \times L}{231}$$

$$C = \frac{(36 \times 24 \times .7854) \times 120}{231} =$$

$$\frac{678.585 \times 120}{231} = \frac{81430.2}{231} = 352\tfrac{1}{2} \text{ gallons}$$

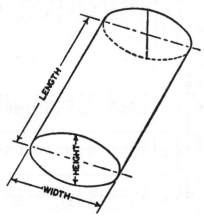

Fig. 16. Elliptical tank.

Spheres

Formula for Surface:

S = surface
D^2 = diameter squared
$S = D^2 \times 3.1416$

Example:

What is the surface of a sphere whose diameter is 4 in.?
$S = D^2 \times 3.1416$
$S = 4^2 \times 3.1416 = 4 \times 4 \times 3.1416$
$= 50.26$ square inches

Formula for Volume:

V = volume
D^3 = cube of the diameter
$V = D^3 \times .5236$

Example:

What is the volume of a sphere whose diameter is 4 in.?
$V = D^3 \times .5236$
$V = 4^3 \times .5236 = 4 \times 4 \times 4 \times .5236$
$= 33.5104$ cubic inches

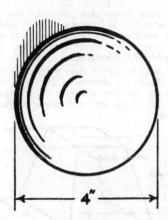

Fig. 17 A sphere.

Frustum-Shaped Tanks

A cone or pyramid with the top cut off is called a frustum. Many tanks, vats, cookers, and similar vessels encountered in steamfitting work are shaped like frustums.

It will be noted that a frustum has two bases as shown in Fig. 18. The formula for the volumes of frustums of both cones and pyramids is given below.

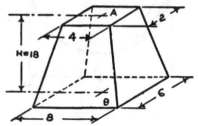

Fig. 18. Frustum-shaped tank.

Formula:

V = volume
H = altitude, or distance between the bases
A = area of the upper base
B = area of the lower base

$$V = \frac{H}{3} \times (A + B + \sqrt{AB})$$

Example:

What is the volume of a frustum which has the dimensions shown in Fig. 18?

$$V = \frac{H}{3} \times (A + B + \sqrt{AB})$$

$$V = \frac{18}{3} (8 + 48 + \sqrt{8 \times 48}) = 6\ (56$$
$$+ \sqrt{384}) = 6\ (56 + 19.6) = 6 \times$$
$$75.6 = 453.6 \text{ cubic inches}$$

FIGURING THE CAPACITY OF A COAL BIN

Formula:

C = capacity
L = length
W = width
H = height
X = weight of 1 cubic foot of coal
C = L x W x H x X

Note: One cubic foot of soft coal weighs 50 pounds. One cubic foot of hard coal weighs 53 pounds.

Example:

How many tons of soft coal will a bin hold which is 10 ft. long, 10 ft. wide, and 8 ft. high?

C = L x W x H x X
C = 10 x 10 x 8 x 50 = 40,000 pounds, or 20 tons of soft coal

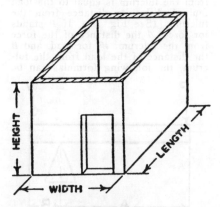

Fig. 19. Coal bin.

LEVERAGE

The force multiplied by its distance from the fulcrum is equal to the load multiplied by its distance from the fulcrum. (See Fig. 20.) If *P* stands for force, *A* the distance of the force from the fulcrum, *W* for load, and *B* the distance of the load from the fulcrum, the following formulas can be used to solve problems involving leverage:

$$P = \frac{W \times B}{A} \qquad W = \frac{P \times A}{B}$$

$$A = \frac{B \times W}{P} \qquad B = \frac{P \times A}{W}$$

Example:

A man weighing 150 lbs. must raise a weight of 800 lbs. which is 6 in. from a fulcrum. What is the length of the lever needed?

$B = 6$ in.

$$A = \frac{B \times W}{P} = \frac{6 \times 800}{150} = \frac{4800}{150} = 32 \text{ in.}$$

Length of lever = $B + A = 6 + 32 = 38$ in.

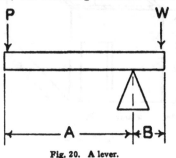

Fig. 20. A lever.

METHODS OF LAYING OUT ANGLES

Laying Out Angles with a Steel Square

Type 1. **Angles less than 45°.** If a 30° angle is desired, obtain the tangent of 30° (.57735) from the Trigonometry Table on p. 190 ff. Move the decimal point of this number one place to the right to obtain the dimension 5.7735 in., or approximately $5\frac{25}{32}$ in. A line drawn from $5\frac{25}{32}$ in. on the blade to 10 in. on the tongue will be at 30° to the tongue of the square. (See Fig. 21.) Follow the same procedure to lay out other angles less than 45°.

Type 2. **Angles greater than 45°** If a 70° angle is desired, subtract 70° from 90° and obtain 20° Find the tangent of 20° (.36397) in the Trigo-

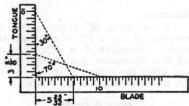

Fig. 21. **Laying out angles with a steel square.**

nometry Table. Move the decimal point of this number one place to the right to obtain the dimension 3.6397 in., or approximately $3\frac{5}{8}$ in. A line drawn from $3\frac{5}{8}$ in. on the tongue to 10 in. on the blade will be at 70° to the tongue. (See Fig. 21.) Follow the same procedure to lay out other angles greater than 45°.

Simplified Method of Laying Out Angles with a Steel Square

Example:

To lay out a 30° angle, obtain dimension *A* for a 30° angle from the table. Dimension *A* is 20¾ in. Lay off this dimension on a straight board and place the square as shown in Fig. 22, thus forming the 30° angle.

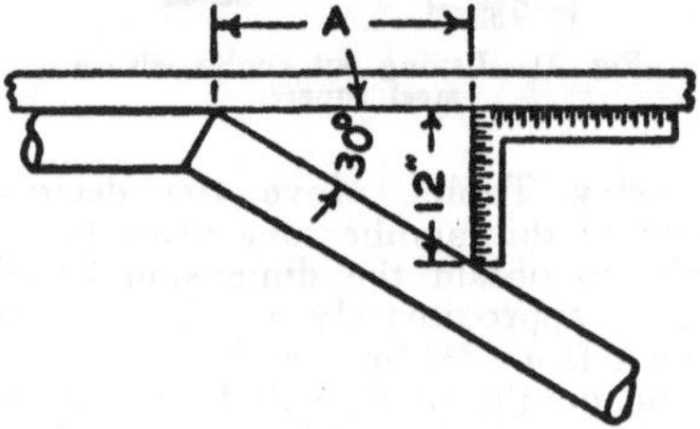

Fig. 22. Laying out a 30° angle with a steel square.

DATA FOR LAYING OUT ANGLES

Angle (Degrees)	A, in Inches	Angle (Degrees)	A, in Inches
5	137⅛	40	14 5/16
10	68 1/16	45	12
15	47¾	50	10 1/16
20	33	55	8⅜
22½	29	60	7
25	25¾	65	5⅝
30	20¾	70	4⅜
35	17⅛	75	3¼

Note: To find dimension *A* for angles that are not shown in the table, multiply the cotangent of the angle by 12 in. (For cotangents of angles, see the Trigonometry Table, pp. 190–194.)

Laying Out Angles with a Two-Foot Rule

Example:

If a 30° angle is desired, open the rule to the chord measurement, namely 3$\frac{3}{32}$ in., given in the table.

CHORD MEASUREMENTS FOR VARIOUS ANGLES

Angle (Degrees)	Chord, in Inches	Angle (Degrees)	Chord, in Inches
5	$\frac{17}{32}$	50	5$\frac{1}{16}$
10	1$\frac{1}{32}$	55	5$\frac{17}{32}$
15	1$\frac{9}{16}$	60	6
20	2$\frac{3}{32}$	65	6$\frac{7}{16}$
25	2$\frac{19}{32}$	70	6$\frac{7}{8}$
30	3$\frac{3}{32}$	75	7$\frac{5}{16}$
35	3$\frac{19}{32}$	80	7$\frac{23}{32}$
40	4$\frac{3}{32}$	85	8$\frac{3}{32}$
45	4$\frac{19}{32}$	90	8$\frac{1}{2}$

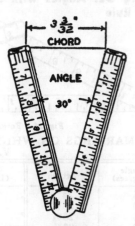

Fig. 23. Forming a 30° angle with a two-foot rule.

Laying Out Angles with a Six-Foot Rule

Example:
For a 45° angle, bend the rule at the first and second joints, setting the end on the marking for the angle, namely 22 31/32 in., given in the table. The desired angle will be formed as shown in Fig. 24.

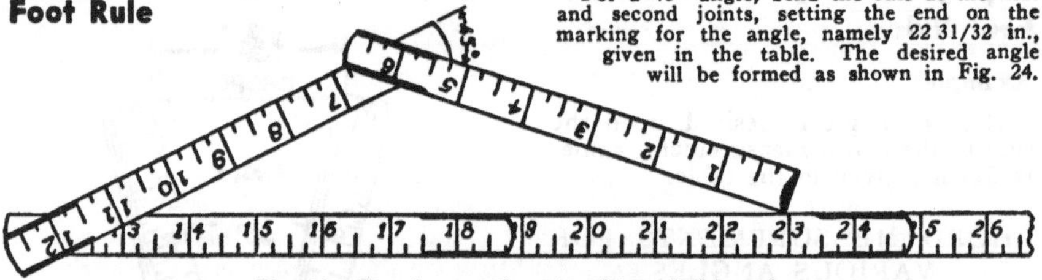

Fig. 24. Forming a 45° angle with a six-foot rule.

MARKINGS ON WHICH END OF RULE IS SET TO FORM VARIOUS ANGLES

Angle (Degrees)	Set On	Angle (Degrees)	Set On	Angle (Degrees)	Set On
5	24	30	23½	60	22¼
10	23$\frac{13}{16}$	35	23$\frac{3}{8}$	65	21$\frac{13}{16}$
15	23⅞	40	23$\frac{1}{16}$	70	21$\frac{11}{16}$
20	23$\frac{25}{32}$	45	22$\frac{31}{32}$	75	21⅜
22½	23$\frac{23}{32}$	50	22¾	80	21$\frac{3}{32}$
25	23⅝	55	22½	90	20$\frac{3}{32}$

METHOD OF MAKING A SQUARE

1. Nail together two straight pieces of 1 x 2 board to form an L, as shown in Fig. 25.

2. Mark off a point 3 ft. from the corner on one of the boards.

3. Mark off a point 4 ft. from the corner on the other board.

4. Cut another board exactly 5 ft. long. Line up this board with the points marked off.

Note: These measurements can be doubled to make a larger square, or they may be cut in half to make a smaller square.

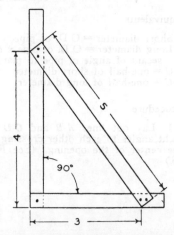

Fig. 25. Square made from wood boards.

METHOD OF LAYING OUT AN ELLIPTICAL-SHAPED HOLE ON STEEL PLATE

Equivalents

Short diameter = O.D. of pipe
Long diameter = O.D. of pipe x co-
  secant of angle of pipe to plate
F-G = one-half of short diameter
E-G = one-half of long diameter

Procedure

1. Lay out lines *A-B* and *C-D* at right angles to each other crossing at the center of the opening. (See Fig. 26.)

2. Lay out the dimensions *F-G* and *E-G* on a flat piece of wood.

3. Draw the curved line at point *G* keeping points *E* and *F* on lines *A-B* and *C-D* as the piece of wood is revolved.

Note: When cutting with the torch, hold the tip at the same angle with the plate as the pipe will be when installed.

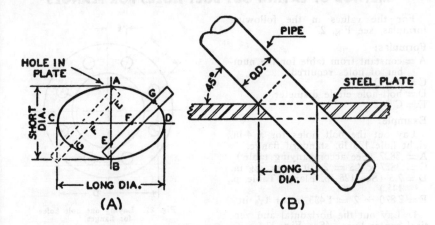

Fig. 26. Laying out an elliptical-shaped hole.

METHOD OF LAYING OUT BOLT HOLES FOR FLANGES

For the values in the following formulas, see Fig. 27.

Formulas:

A = constant from table for the number of holes required
C = A x D
D = bolt-hole circle diameter
E = C ÷ 2

Example:

Lay out the bolt holes for a 4-in. eight hole 125 lb. standard flange.
A = .3827 (See accompanying table.)
C = .3827 x 7.5 = 2.870 in. or 2⅞ in.
D = 7.5 (See 125 lb. Flange Table, p. 145.)
E = 2.870 ÷ 2 = 1.435 in. or 1$\frac{7}{16}$ in.

1. Lay out the horizontal and vertical center lines. (See Fig. 27.)

2. Obtain the bolt-hole circle diameter D from the table on flanges

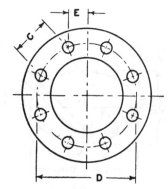

Fig. 27. Laying out bolt holes for flanges.

for the flange size required. (See page 145.)

3. Scribe the bolt hole circle with a scriber from the center of the flange.

4. Determine the value of C, using the above formula. Then divide C by 2 to determine dimension E.

5. Lay out dimension E horizontally from the vertical center line on the bolt hole circle, locating the center of the first bolt hole.

6. Set the scribers for dimension C. Now place one point of the scriber on the center line of the first bolt hole and scribe an arc on the bolt hole center line locating the center of the second bolt hole. Then place the scriber point on the center of the second bolt hole, and scribe an arc on the bolt hole center line locating the

center of the third bolt hole. Locate the rest of the bolt hole centers around the circumference in this manner.

CONSTANTS FOR FIGURING BOLT HOLE LOCATIONS

Number of Bolt Holes	Constant A	Number of Bolt Holes	Constant A
4	.7071	24	.1305
8	.3827	28	.1120
12	.2588	32	.0980
16	.1951	36	.0872
20	.1564	40	.0785
		44	.0713

Note: For any number of holes not shown, multiply the sine of one-half the angle between the holes by the diameter of the bolt hole circle, for Constant A.

METHOD OF LAYING OUT RING GASKETS

The method of laying out a ring gasket for a standard companion flange is as follows:

1. Obtain dimensions A and B from the table and locate points for nails D, E, and F, on a 1×2 board. (See Fig. 28 (A).)

2. Drive nails through the points marked off.

3. Place the board on the gasket material. Using nail D as a compass point, revolve the board 360° around the point. Nails E and F will scribe the lines for the ring gasket. (See Fig. 28 (B).)

RING-GASKET DIMENSIONS

Pipe Size, in Inches	A, in Inches	B, in Inches	C, in Inches
2	1	1	2
2½	1¼	1⅛	2⅜
3	1½	1⅛	2⅝
3½	1¾	1⅜	3⅛
4	2	1⅜	3⅜
5	2½	1⅜	3⅞
6	3	1⅜	4⅜
8	4	1½	5½
10	5	1⅝	6⅝
12	6	2	8

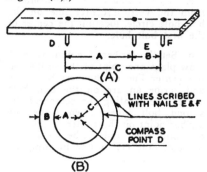

Fig. 28. Laying out ring gaskets.

FIGURING ROD LENGTHS FOR U BOLTS

For the values in the following formulas, see Fig. 29.

Formulas:

A = D + F

B = one-half outside diameter of the pipe

C = nut thickness

D = outside diameter of the pipe

E = amount of rod protruding through the nut

F = diameter of the rod

L = 1.571 x A

T = thickness of the plate

W = 2B + 2C + 2E + L + 2T
 (length of rod required)

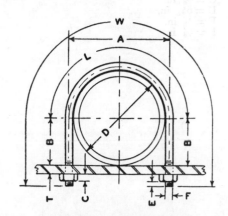

Fig. 29. Values for U bolt formulas.

Example:

Determine the length of ⅝-in. rod required to make a U bolt for 6-in. pipe, through a ¼-in. plate with ⅜ in. of rod protruding through the nut.

A $= 6\frac{5}{8}$ in. $+ \frac{5}{8}$ in. $= 7\frac{1}{4}$ in.

B $= 6\frac{5}{8}$ in. $\div 2 = 3\frac{5}{16}$ in.

C $= \frac{5}{8}$ in.

D $= 6\frac{5}{8}$ in.

E $= \frac{3}{8}$ in.

F $= \frac{5}{8}$ in.

L $= 1.571 \times 7.25 = 11.389$ in. or $11\frac{3}{8}$ in.

T $= \frac{1}{4}$ in.

W $= 6\frac{5}{8}$ in. $+ 1\frac{1}{4}$ in. $+ \frac{3}{4}$ in. $+ 11\frac{3}{8}$ in. $+ \frac{1}{2}$ in. $= 20\frac{1}{2}$ in.

Cut rod $20\frac{1}{2}$ in. long.

2

PIPE-FITTING CALCULATION

CALCULATED 45° OFFSETS

When the set or travel of a 45° offset is known, the other may be found by use of the table given below.

Example:

To find the length of travel for a 45° offset with a set of 4 ft. 8¾ in.:

1. Change the dimension of the set to inches: 4 ft. 8¾ in. = 56¾ in.

2. Locate 56¾ in. in the table under the heading, "Set," and obtain the travel, 80.244 in., in the column to the right.

3. Referring to the decimal equivalent chart (p. 178), change the decimal to a fraction: .244 in. = ¼ in. The

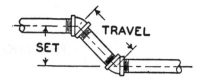

Fig. 30. Piping offset.

travel then is 80¼ in. or 6 ft. 8¼ in. center to center.

To find the set when the travel is known, reverse the above procedure.

SET AND TRAVEL RELATIONSHIPS IN INCHES FOR 45° OFFSETS

Set	Travel	Set	Travel	Set	Travel
2	2.828	1/4	15.907	1/2	28.987
1/4	3.181	1/2	16.261	3/4	29.340
1/2	3.531	3/4	16.614	21	29.694
3/4	3.888	12	16.968	1/4	30.047
3	4.242	1/4	17.321	1/2	30.401
1/4	4.575	1/2	17.675	3/4	30.754
1/2	4.949	3/4	18.028	22	31.108
3/4	5.302	13	18.382	1/4	31.461
4	5.656	1/4	18.735	1/2	31.815
1/4	6.009	1/2	19.089	3/4	32.168
1/2	6.363	3/4	19.442	23	32.522
3/4	6.716	14	19.796	1/4	32.875
5	7.070	1/4	20.149	1/2	33.229
1/4	7.423	1/2	20.503	3/4	33.582
1/2	7.777	3/4	20.856	24	33.936
3/4	8.130	15	21.210	1/4	34.289
6	8.484	1/4	21.563	1/2	34.643
1/4	8.837	1/2	21.917	3/4	34.996
1/2	9.191	3/4	22.270	25	35.350
3/4	9.544	16	22.624	1/4	35.703
7	9.898	1/4	22.977	1/2	36.057
1/4	10.251	1/2	23.331	3/4	36.410
1/2	10.605	3/4	23.684	26	36.764
3/4	10.958	17	24.038	1/4	37.117
8	11.312	1/4	24.391	1/2	37.471
1/4	11.665	1/2	24.745	3/4	37.824
1/2	12.019	3/4	25.098	27	38.178
3/4	12.372	18	25.452	1/4	38.531
9	12.726	1/4	25.805	1/2	38.885
1/4	13.079	1/2	26.159	3/4	39.238
1/2	13.433	3/4	26.512	28	39.592
3/4	13.786	19	26.866	1/4	39.945
10	14.140	1/4	27.219	1/2	40.299
1/4	14.493	1/2	27.573	3/4	40.652
1/2	14.847	3/4	27.926	29	41.006
3/4	15.200	20	28.280	1/4	41.359
11	15.554	1/4	28.635	1/2	41.713

SET AND TRAVEL RELATIONSHIPS IN INCHES FOR 45° OFFSETS (Cont'd)

Set	Travel	Set	Travel	Set	Travel
3/4	42.066	39	55.146	1/4	68.225
30	42.420	1/4	55.499	1/2	68.579
1/4	42.773	1/2	55.853	3/4	68.932
1/2	43.127	3/4	56.206	49	69.286
3/4	43.480	40	56.560	1/4	69.639
31	43.834	1/4	56.913	1/2	69.993
1/4	44.187	1/2	57.267	3/4	70.346
1/2	44.541	3/4	57.620	50	70.700
3/4	44.894	41	57.974	1/4	71.053
32	45.248	1/4	58.327	1/2	71.407
1/4	45.601	1/2	58.681	3/4	71.760
1/2	45.955	3/4	59.034	51	72.114
3/4	46.308	42	59.388	1/4	72.467
33	46.662	1/4	59.741	1/2	72.821
1/4	47.015	1/2	60.095	3/4	73.174
1/2	47.369	3/4	60.448	52	73.528
3/4	47.722	43	60.802	1/4	73.881
34	48.076	1/4	61.155	1/2	74.235
1/4	48.429	1/2	61.509	3/4	74.588
1/2	48.783	3/4	61.862	53	74.942
3/4	49.136	44	62.216	1/4	75.295
35	49.490	1/4	62.569	1/2	75.649
1/4	49.843	1/2	62.923	3/4	76.002
1/2	50.197	3/4	63.276	54	76.356
3/4	50.550	45	63.630	1/4	76.709
36	50.904	1/4	63.983	1/2	77.063
1/4	51.257	1/2	64.337	3/4	77.416
1/2	51.611	3/4	64.690	55	77.770
3/4	51.964	46	65.044	1/4	78.123
37	52.318	1/4	65.397	1/2	78.477
1/4	52.671	1/2	65.751	3/4	78.830
1/2	53.025	3/4	66.104	56	79.184
3/4	53.378	47	66.458	1/4	79.537
38	53.732	1/4	66.811	1/2	79.891
1/4	54.085	1/2	67.165	3/4	80.244
1/2	54.439	3/4	67.518	57	80.598
3/4	54.792	48	67.872	1/4	80.951

SET AND TRAVEL RELATIONSHIPS IN INCHES FOR 45° OFFSETS (Cont'd)

Set	Travel	Set	Travel	Set	Travel
1/2	81.305	3/4	94.384	85	120.190
3/4	81.658	67	94.738	86	121.604
58	82.012	1/4	95.091	87	123.018
1/4	82.365	1/2	95.445	88	124.432
1/2	82.719	3/4	95.798	89	125.846
3/4	83.072	68	96.152	90	127.260
59	83.426	1/4	96.505	91	128.674
1/4	83.779	1/2	96.859	92	130.088
1/2	84.133	3/4	97.212	93	131.502
3/4	84.486	69	97.566	94	132.916
60	84.840	1/4	97.919	95	134.330
1/4	85.193	1/2	98.273	96	135.744
1/2	85.547	3/4	98.626	97	137.158
3/4	85.900	70	98.980	98	138.572
61	86.254	1/4	99.333	99	139.986
1/4	86.607	1/2	99.687	100	141.400
1/2	86.961	3/4	100.040	101	142.814
3/4	87.314	71	100.394	102	144.228
62	87.668	1/4	100.747	103	145.672
1/4	88.021	1/2	101.101	104	147.056
1/2	88.375	3/4	101.454	105	148.470
3/4	88.728	72	101.808	106	149.884
63	89.082	1/4	102.165	107	151.298
1/4	89.435	1/2	102.515	108	152.712
1/2	89.789	3/4	102.868	109	154.126
3/4	90.142	73	103.222	110	155.540
64	90.496	74	104.636	111	156.954
1/4	90.849	75	106.050	112	158.368
1/2	91.203	76	107.464	113	159.782
3/4	91.556	77	108.878	114	161.196
65	91.910	78	110.292	115	162.610
1/4	92.263	79	111.706	116	164.024
1/2	92.617	80	113.120	117	165.438
3/4	92.970	81	114.534	118	166.852
66	93.324	82	115.948	119	168.266
1/4	93.677	83	117.362	120	169.680
1/2	94.031	84	118.776		

SIMPLE OFFSETS

All piping offsets are based on the right triangle. The angle of fitting is the number of degrees the piping changes direction. Fig. 31 shows a 22½° offset — the piping changes direction 22½° and the fittings at *A* and *B* are 22½° ells.

Simple offsets may be calculated by use of the table given below.

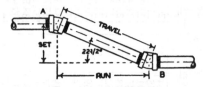

Fig. 31. Piping offset.

MULTIPLIERS FOR CALCULATING SIMPLE OFFSETS

To Find Side*	When Known Side Is	Multiply Side	For 60° Ells By	For 45° Ells By	For 30° Ells By	For 22½° Ells By	For 11¼° Ells By	For 5⅝° Ells By
T	S	S	1.155	1.414	2.000	2.613	5.125	10.187
S	T	T	.866	.707	.500	.383	.195	.098
R	S	S	.577	1.000	1.732	2.414	5.027	10.158
S	R	R	1.732	1.000	.577	.414	.198	.098
T	R	R	2.000	1.414	1.155	1.082	1.019	1.004
R	T	T	.500	.707	.866	.924	.980	.995

*S = set, R = run, T = travel.

Use of Table:

Find the side of the triangle that is needed in the first column. Find the known side in the second column. Continue across in that row to the column headed with the angle of fitting to be used and read the constant. Multiply the constant by the known side and the answer will be the length of the side needed.

Example:

What is the length of side T for a 30° offset if side S is 15 in.?

1. The side needed, T, and the side known, S, are found in the first row in the first and second columns.

2. Continuing across in the same row to the 30° ell column, the constant is found to be 2.

3. Multiplying the constant 2 by 15 (the known side S), side T is found to be 30 in., center to center.

TWO-PIPE EQUAL-SPREAD OFFSETS

Two-Pipe 22½° Equal-Spread Offset

Note: 22½° fittings to be used.

Formulas:

A = spread
S = set
T = S x 2.613
R = S x 2.414
F = A x .1989
D = T

T and D are the same length.

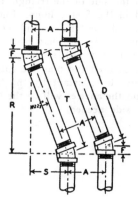

Fig. 32. Two-pipe 22½°
equal-spread offset.

Two-Pipe 30° Equal-Spread Offset

Note: 30° fittings to be used.

Formulas:

A = spread
S = set
T = S x 2.000
R = S x 1.732
F = A x .2679
D = T

T and D are the same length.

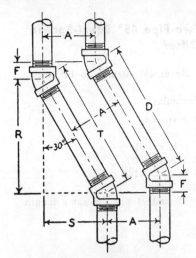

Fig. 33. Two-pipe 30° equal-spread offset.

Two-Pipe 45° Equal-Spread Offset

Note: 45° fittings to be used.

Formulas:

A = spread
S = set
T = S x 1.414
R = S x 1.000
F = A x .4142
D = T

    T and D are the same length.

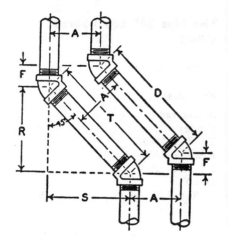

Fig. 34. Two-pipe 45° equal-spread offset.

Two-Pipe 60° Equal-Spread Offset

Note: 60° fittings to be used.

Formulas:

A = spread
S = set
T = S x 1.155
R = S x .5773
F = A x .5773
D = T
   T and D are the same length.

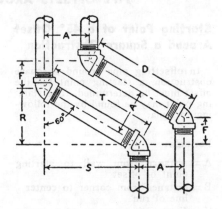

Fig. 35. Two-pipe 60° equal-spread offset.

PIPE OFFSETS AROUND OBSTRUCTIONS

Starting Point of a 45° Offset Around a Square Obstruction

In offsetting pipe around a square obstruction, a starting point for the offset must be determined. The starting point may be found by the following formula:

Formula:

A = distance from wall to starting point of offset

B = distance from corner to center line of run

C = distance from corner to center of pipe

A = B + (C x 1.414)

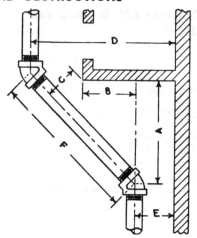

Fig. 36. Forty-five degree offset around square obstruction.

Example:

Find distance *A* if *B* is 12 in. and *C* is 6 in.

$$A = B + (C \times 1.414)$$

$A = 12 + (6 \times 1.414) = 12 + 8\frac{1}{2} = 20\frac{1}{2}$ in. Hence, the center of the 45° ell is 20½ in. from the wall.

Note: $F = (D - E) \times 1.414$

Starting Point of a 45° Offset Around a Tank

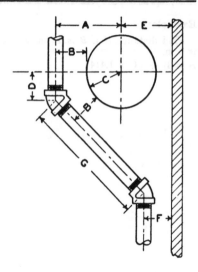

Formulas:

A = distance from center of tank to center of pipe

B = distance from side of tank to center of pipe

C = ½ of the diameter of the tank

D = distance from center line of tank to starting point of offset

$A = B + C$

$D = A \times .4142$

Example:

Find D if C is 18 in. and B is 8 in.

$A = B + C = 8 + 18 = 26$ in.

$D = A \times .4142 = 26 \times .4142 = 10\frac{3}{4}$ in.

Hence the center of the 45° fitting is 10¾ in. from the center line of the tank.

Note: $G = (A + E - F) \times 1.414$

Fig. 37. Forty-five degree offset around a tank.

Three-Pipe 45° Equal-Spread Offset Around a Tank

Dimensions for Layout in Fig. 38:

A = diameter of tank + 3 + 5 = 18 + 3 + 5 = 26 in.

B = radius of tank + 5 x .4142 = 9 + 5 x .4142 = 5.798 or 5¾ in.

C = A − 6 x 1.414 = (26 − 6) x 1.414 = 28.28 or 28¼ in.

D = A + 9 − 15 x 1.414 = 20 x 1.414 = 28.28 or 28¼ in.

E = A + 9 + 9 − 24 x 1.414 = 20 x 1.414 = 28.28 or 28¼ in.

F = 9 x .4142 = 3.727 or 3¾ in.

G = 9 + 9 x .4142 = 7.455 or 7½ in.

Note: Pipes *C*, *D*, and *E* are the same length in a problem of this type.

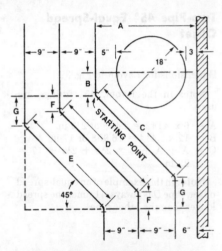

Fig. 38. Three-pipe 45° equal-spread offset around a tank.

Two-Pipe 45° Equal-Spread Offset

Dimensions for Layout in Fig. 39:

Note: In the layout, 45° fittings are used.

A = 6 x .4142 = 2.485 or 2½ in.
B = 12 x 1.414 = 16.968 or 17 in.
C = A + A + B = 2½ + 2½ + 17 = 22 in.

Note: In this example of an equal-spread offset, Pipe *D* is always .41 times the spread longer than the other pipe.

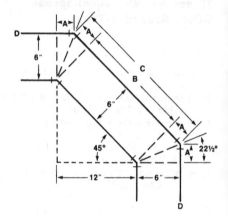

Fig. 39. Two-pipe 45° equal-spread offset.

Three-Pipe Equal-Spread Offset Around a Square Obstruction

Example:

Fig. 40 shows a three-pipe 45° equal-spread offset. The outside line is to be 8 in. from the wall and 5 in. from the corner. The spreads are to be 9 in. Find the lengths of pieces C, D, and E.

$A = 9 \times .4142 = 3.727$ or $3\frac{3}{4}$ in.

$B = A + A = 3\frac{3}{4} + 3\frac{3}{4} = 7\frac{1}{2}$ in.

$C = 12 \times 1.414 = 16.968$ or 17 in.

$E = (12 + 9 + 9 - B) \times 1.414$
$= (30 - 7\frac{1}{2}) \times 1.414$
$= 22.5 \times 1.414 = 31.815$ or $31\frac{13}{16}$ in.

$D = (12 + 9 - A) \times 1.414$
$= (12 + 9 - 3\frac{3}{4}) \times 1.414$
$= 17\frac{1}{4} \times 1.414 = 24.391$ or $24\frac{3}{8}$ in.

$F = 16 - 8 = 8$ in.

$G = H \times 1.414 + F = 5 \times 1.414 + 8$
$= 7 + 8 = 15$ in.

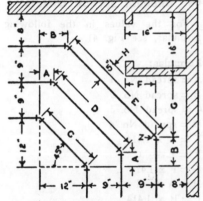

Fig. 40. Three pipe equal-spread offset around a square obstruction.

Note: Some numbers are adjusted to the nearest fraction or whole number.

45° Unequal Spread Offsets

For the values in the following formulas, see Fig. 41.

Formulas:

$A =$ spread No. 1
$B =$ spread No. 2
$C =$ spread No. 3
$D =$ spread No. 4
$E = A \times 1.414$
$F = E - C$
$G = F \times 1.414$
$H = A - G$
$J = B \times 1.414$
$K = D - J$
$L = K \times 1.414$
$M = L + B + H$

Example:

Find the lengths of H and M for a 45° unequal spread offset when $A = 9$ in., $B = 8$ in., $C = 10$ in., and $D = 15$ in.

$A = 9$ in.
$B = 8$ in.
$C = 10$ in.
$D = 15$ in.
$E = 9 \times 1.414 = 12.726$ in.
$F = 12.726 - 10 = 2.726$ in.
$G = 2.726 \times 1.414 = 3.854$ in.
$H = 9 - 3.854 = 5.146$ in. or $5\frac{1}{8}$ in.
$J = 8 \times 1.414 = 11.312$ in.
$K = 15 - 11.312 = 3.688$ in.
$L = 3.688 \times 1.414 = 5.214$ in.
$M = 5.214 + 8 + 5.146 = 18.360$ in. or $18\frac{3}{8}$ in.

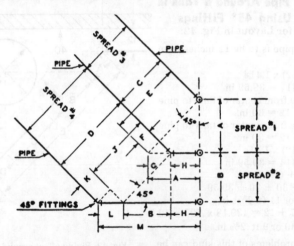

Fig. 41. 45° unequal-spread offset.

Offsetting Pipe Around a Tank in a Corner Using 45° Fittings

Dimensions for Layout in Fig. 42:

Note: The pipe is to be 12 inches from the tank.

$A = (40 - 12)$ x 1.414

  = 28 x 1.414 = 39.59 in.

$B =$ distance from center of tank to pipe

  = 18 + 12 = 30 in.

$C =$ distance from center of tank to pipe

  = 18 + 12 = 30 in.

$D = (40 - 12)$ x 1.414

  = 28 x 1.414 = 39.59 in.

$E = A + B + C + D$

  = 39.59 + 30 + 30 + 39.59

  = 139.18 or 11 ft. 7 3/16 in.

$F = E$ x .707 + 12 = 139.18 x .707 + 12

  = 110.40 or 9 ft. 2 3/8 in.

Note: All problems of this kind can be solved the same way.

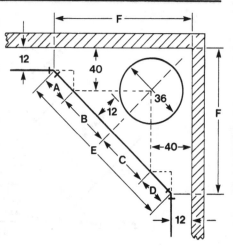

Fig. 42. Piping offset around a tank in a corner with 45° fittings.

SPECIAL OFFSETS

Example:

Find the length of A and B for the layout shown in Fig. 43. Forty-five degree fittings are to be used.

$A = C \div 2.414$
$A = 72 \div 2.414 = 29.82$ in. or
$\qquad 29^{13}/_{16}$ in.
$B = 10$ ft. $- (A \times .707)$
$B = 120$ in. $- (29.82 \times .707) = 120 -$
$\qquad 21.083 = 98.917$ in. or $98^{15}/_{16}$ in.

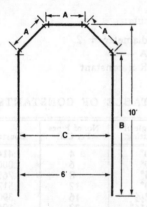

Fig. 43. Special offset.

TANK COILS

Formula:

A = diameter ÷ 2
R = A — B
L = R x constant

TABLE OF CONSTANTS

Angle of Fitting	No. of Pipes Per Coil	Constants
90°	4	1.4142
60°	6	1.0000
45°	8	.7653
30°	12	.5176
22½°	16	.3902
11¼°	32	.1960
5⅝°	64	.0981

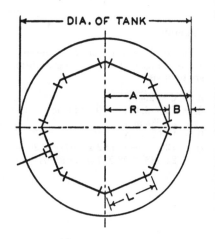

Fig. 44. Tank-coil.

Example:

The diameter of a tank is 72 in. and distance *B* is 12 in. If 45° fittings are to be used for the tank coil, how long should the pipe be?

A = diameter ÷ 2
A = 72 ÷ 2 = 36
R = A — B
R = 36 — 12 = 24
L = R x constant
L = 24 x .7653 = 18⅜ in. — length of each piece of pipe, center to center

ROLLING OFFSETS

Finding Travel and Run for a Rolling Offset

Formula:

$$A = \sqrt{roll^2 + set^2}$$

Travel = A x cosecant of angle of fitting (See Trigonometry Table.)

Run = A x cotangent of angle of fitting (See Trigonometry Table.)

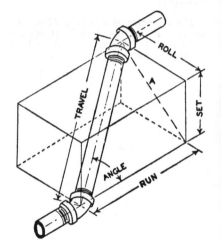

Fig. 45. Rolling offset.

Example:

The roll of a 45° offset is 8 in. and the set is 15 in. Find the length of travel and run.

$$A = \sqrt{roll^2 + set^2}$$
$$A = \sqrt{8^2 + 15^2} = \sqrt{289} = 17 \text{ in.}$$

Travel = A x cosecant of angle of fitting

Travel = 17 x 1.414 = 24$\frac{1}{32}$ in., center to center

Run = A x cotangent of angle of fitting

Run = 17 x 1.000 = 17 in., center to center

Simplified Method of Figuring a Rolling Offset

Use a steel square, the corner of a bench, the corner of a room, or anything that forms a 90° angle.

Lay out the roll on one side of the square and the set on the other side. Then measure across these two points with a rule and multiply the measurement by the constant for the angle of fitting required.

CONSTANTS FOR COMMON ANGLES

Angle	Constant
5⅝°	10.207
11¼°	5.125
22½°	2.613
30°	2.000
45°	1.414
60°	1.154

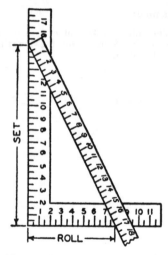

Fig. 46. Laying out a rolling offset with a steel square.

Example:

Lay out a 45° offset which has a set of 15 in., a roll of 8 in.

Lay off 15 in. on one side of the square and 8 in. on the other side. Measure the distance between the points marked off. Multiply this distance, 17 in., by the constant 1.414 and obtain 24 1/32 in., the length of the pipe center to center.

3

PIPE-WELDING LAYOUT

GENERAL

The purpose of this section is to simplify pipe layouts. Procedures are presented for laying out, without templates, fittings made from pipe. The layout equipment includes only a square, a level, a wrap around, a strip of paper, and a piece of soapstone or chalk. Accuracy, of course, is required when the methods explained in the section are employed.

THE WRAP AROUND

The wrap around, sometimes referred to as a run around, is a flat strip of flexible material about $\frac{1}{16}$ to $\frac{1}{8}$ in. thick, 3 to 4 in. wide, and 18 in. or more long. It is made of any composition gasket material or leather belting. The edges must be perfectly straight. The length may vary. However, the wrap around should be long enough to go around the pipe $1\frac{1}{2}$ times so that it may be lined up and thus make it possible to obtain a straight line around the pipe.

When laying out a straight line around a pipe, place the wrap around on the pipe at the location of the center line and line up the edges. (See Fig. 47.) Then with a piece of soap-

stone pencil, draw a chalk line around the pipe using the edge of the wrap around as a guide.

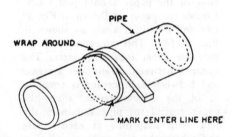

Fig. 47. Using a wrap around.

DIVISION OF PIPE SURFACE INTO FOUR EQUAL PARTS

To divide the outside circumference of a pipe into four equal parts, wrap a strip of paper around the pipe and tear off the part that overlaps. The ends of the paper should just touch. Double the paper as shown in Fig. 48 (*A*) and double it again as shown in Fig. 48 (*B*). This procedure will divide the paper into four parts. The distance between an end and a crease and between each crease is equal to ¼ of the circumference. Place the paper around the pipe and mark the pipe with soapstone at each crease and where the two ends meet. (See Fig. 48 (*C*).)

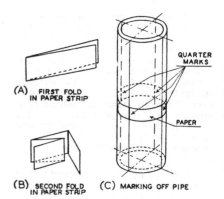

(A) FIRST FOLD IN PAPER STRIP

(B) SECOND FOLD IN PAPER STRIP

(C) MARKING OFF PIPE

QUARTER MARKS

PAPER

Fig. 48. Dividing pipe surface into four equal parts.

TURNS

Formula for Angle of Cut

The angle of cut is the angle the pipe must be cut to form the necessary turn. The following formula is used to find the angle of cut for all turns fabricated from pipe.

Formula:

$$\text{Angle of cut} = \frac{\text{number of degrees of turn}}{\text{number of welds} \times 2}$$

Example:

Find the angle of cut for a two-piece 90° turn. (See Fig. 49.)

Note: One weld is required for a two-piece 90° turn.

Applying the above formula:

$$\text{Angle of cut} = \frac{90}{2 \times 1} = \frac{90}{2} = 45°$$

Example:

Find the angle of cut for a four-piece 90° turn. (See Fig. 50.)

Note: Three welds are required for a four-piece 90° turn.

Applying the above formula:

$$\text{Angle of cut} = \frac{90}{2 \times 3} = \frac{90}{6} = 15°$$

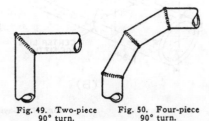

Fig. 49. Two-piece 90° turn.   Fig. 50. Four-piece 90° turn.

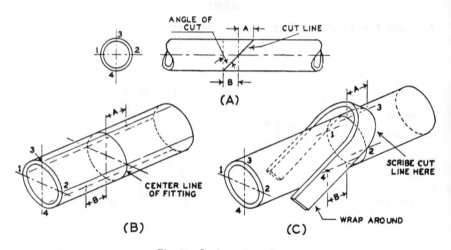

Fig. 51. Laying out cut lines.

FACTORS FOR ANGLES OF CUT

Angle of Cut	Factor	Angle of Cut	Factor	Angle of Cut	Factor	Angle of Cut	Factor
5°	.08749	15°	.26795	25°	.46631	35°	.70021
5° 30′	.09629	15° 30′	.27732	25° 30′	.47697	35° 30′	.71329
6	.10510	16	.28674	26	.48773	36	.72654
6 30	.11393	16 30	.29621	26 30	.49858	36 30	.73996
7	.12278	17	.30573	27	.50952	37	.75355
7 30	.13165	17 30	.31530	27 30	.52057	37 30	.76733
8	.14054	18	.32492	28	.53171	38	.78128
8 30	.14945	18 30	.33459	28 30	.54295	38 30	.79543
9	.15838	19	.34433	29	.55431	39	.80978
9 30	.16734	19 30	.35412	29 30	.56577	39 30	.82424
10	.17633	20	.36397	30	.57735	40	.83910
10 30	.18534	20 30	.37388	30 30	.58904	40 30	.85408
11	.19438	21	.38386	31	.60086	41	.86929
11 30	.20345	21 30	.39391	31 30	.61280	41 30	.88472
12	.21256	22	.40403	32	.62487	42	.90040
12 30	.22169	22 30	.41421	32 30	.63707	42 30	.91633
13	.23087	23	.42447	33	.64941	43	.93251
13 30	.24008	23 30	.43481	33 30	.66188	43 30	.94896
14	.24933	24	.44523	34	.67451	44	.96569
14 30	.25862	24 30	.45573	34 30	.68728	45	1.00000

Laying Out Cut Lines for a Two-Piece 90° Turn

1. To draw the center line of the turn, place a wrap around on the pipe at the center of the turn. (See p. 73.) Using the wrap around as a guide, draw a straight line around the pipe with soapstone or chalk.

2. Divide the surface of the pipe into four equal parts on the center line of the turn. (See p. 74.) Number these lines as shown in Fig. 51 (*B*) — line No. 3 on top, No. 4 on bottom, and Nos. 1 and 2 on the sides.

3. Find the angle of cut. (See p. 75.)

4. Find dimensions *A* and *B* using the following formula:

$$A \text{ and } B = \frac{\text{O.D. of pipe x factor for angle of cut}}{2}$$

Note: Obtain the factor for the angle of cut from the table on page 77.

5. On lines 3 and 4, lay out dimensions *A* and *B* from the center line of turn.

6. Place the wrap around on the pipe and line it up with the points on lines 3, 2, and 1. (See Fig. 51 (*C*).) Draw a line with a soapstone or chalk connecting these three points. Then revolve the wrap around 180° and line it up with the points on lines 4, 2, and 1. Connect these three points. In this manner a chalk line known as the cut line will be drawn around the pipe.

Note: When using a cutting torch, make a miter cut. To make a miter cut, point the cutting tip at all times to the line on the opposite side of the pipe; then bevel the edges after the cut has been made.

Note: Two pipes cut as described above will form a 90° turn.

Example:

Lay out a two-piece 90° turn on 4-in. pipe. (See Fig. 52.) Follow the above procedure. Note the following:

In step 3—

$$\text{Angle of cut} = \frac{\text{number of degrees of turn}}{\text{number of welds} \times 2}$$

$$\text{Angle of cut} = \frac{90}{2 \times 1} = 45°$$

In step 4—

$$A \text{ and } B = \frac{\text{O.D. of pipe} \times \text{factor for angle of cut}}{2}$$

O.D. of 4-in. pipe = 4.5 in. (See table on p. 148 f.)

Factor for 45° angle of cut = 1.000 (See table on p. 77.)

$$A \text{ and } B = \frac{4.5 \times 1.0000}{2} = \frac{4.5}{2} = 2.25 \text{ in.}$$

or 2¼ in.

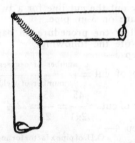

Fig. 52. Two-piece 90° turn.

Laying Out Cut Lines for a Two-Piece 45° Turn

The procedure for laying out the cut line for a two-piece 45° turn (see Fig. 53) is the same as for a two-piece 90° turn. (See pp. 78-79.) The only difference is in the angle of cut.

Example:

Lay out the cut line for a two-piece 45° turn on 3-in. pipe.

Follow the procedure on pages 78-79. Note the following:
In step 3—

$$\text{Angle of cut} = \frac{\text{number of degrees of turn}}{\text{number of welds x 2}}$$

$$\text{Angle of cut} = \frac{45}{2\text{x}1} = \frac{45}{2} = 22\frac{1}{2}°$$

In step 4—

$$A \text{ and } B = \frac{\text{O.D. of pipe x factor for angle of cut}}{2}$$

O.D. of 3-in. pipe = 3.5 in. (See table on p. 148 f.)

Factor for 22½° angle of cut = .4142 (See table on p. 77.)

A and $B =$

$$\frac{3.5 \text{ x } .4142}{2} = \frac{1.449}{2} = .725 \text{ or}$$

$$\frac{23}{32} \text{ in.}$$

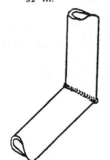

Fig. 53. Two-piece 45° turn.

Laying Out Cut Lines for a Four-Piece 90° Turn

The procedure for laying out the cut line for a four-piece 90° turn (see Fig. 54) is the same as that for a two-piece 90° turn. (See pp. 78-79.) The only difference is in the angle of cut.

Example:

Lay out the cut lines for a four-piece 90° turn on a 6-in. pipe.

Follow the procedure on pages 76 to 79. Note the following:

In step 3—

$$\text{Angle of cut} = \frac{\text{number of degrees of turn}}{\text{number of welds} \times 2}$$

$$\text{Angle of cut} = \frac{90}{2 \times 3} = \frac{90}{6} = 15°$$

In step 4—

$$A \text{ and } B = \frac{\text{O.D. of pipe} \times \text{factor for angle of cut}}{2}$$

O.D. of 6 in. pipe = 6.625 in. (See table on p. 148 f.)

Factor for 15° angle of cut = .26795. (See table on p. 77.)

$$A \text{ and } B = \frac{6.625 \times .26795}{2} = \frac{1.775}{2} = .8875 \text{ or } \frac{7}{8} \text{ in.}$$

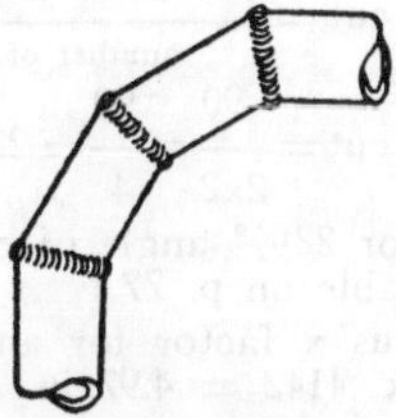

Fig. 54. Four-piece 90° turn.

Determining the Length of Cut Pieces for a Three-Piece 90° Turn

Formulas:

A = radius x factor for angle of cut
B = A x 2

Example:

Find the dimensions of *A* and *B* for a three-piece 90° turn with a 12-in. radius. (See Fig. 55.)

$$\text{Angle of cut} = \frac{\text{number of degrees of turn}}{\text{number of welds x 2}}$$

$$\text{Angle of cut} = \frac{90}{2x2} = \frac{90}{4} = 22\frac{1}{2}°$$

Factor for 22½° angle of cut = .4142 (See table on p. 77.)

A = radius x factor for angle of cut
A = 12 x .4142 = 4.97 in. or 5 in.
B = A x 2
B = 5 x 2 = 10 in. center to center

Note: The minimum radius for a three-piece turn is 6 times the outside diameter of the pipe.

Note: The cut lines are laid out as explained on pages 78-79.

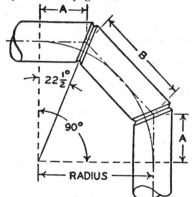

Fig. 55. Three-piece 90° turn.

Determining the Length of Cut Pieces for a Four-Piece 90° Turn

Formulas:

A = radius x factor for angle of cut
B = A x 2

Example:

Find the dimensions of *A* and *B* for a four-piece 90° turn with a 40-in. radius. (See Fig. 56.)

$$\text{Angle of cut} = \frac{\text{number of degrees of turn}}{\text{number of welds x 2}}$$

$$\text{Angle of cut} = \frac{90}{2 \text{x} 3} = \frac{90}{6} = 15°$$

Factor for 15° angle of cut = .26795 (See p. 77.)

A = radius x factor for angle of cut
A = 40 x .26795 = 10.718 or $10\frac{23}{32}$ in.
B = A x 2
B = 10.718 x 2 = 21.436 or $21\frac{7}{16}$ in.

Note: Cut lines are laid out as explained on pages 78-79.

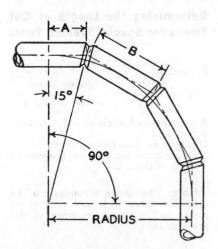

Fig. 56. Four-piece 90° turn.

Determining the Length of Cut Pieces for Special Welded Turns

Formulas:

$$\text{Angle of cut} = \frac{\text{degrees of turn}}{\text{number of welds x 2}}$$

A = tangent of angle of cut x radius
B = A x 2
D = outside diameter of pipe
Measure-back distance = tangent of angle of cut x D

Note: The above formulas can be used for turns with any number of pieces and with any number of degrees of turn.

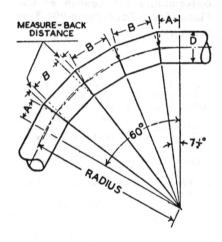

Fig. 57. Special welded turn.

LAYING OUT CUT LINES FOR MITER TURNS ON LARGE PIPE WITH 16 DIVISIONS

For the values in the following formulas, see Fig. 58.

Formulas:

Ordinate No. 1 = center of fitting
Ordinate No. 2 = outside diameter x .1913 x tangent of angle of cut
Ordinate No. 3 = outside diameter x .3535 x tangent of angle of cut
Ordinate No. 4 = outside diameter x .4619 x tangent of angle of cut
Ordinate No. 5 = outside diameter x .5000 x tangent of angle of cut

Example:

Lay out a cut line on 10-in. pipe for a 40° angle of cut.

Outside diameter of 10-in. pipe = 10.75 in.

Tangent of a 40° angle = .83910 (See table on p. 77.)

Ordinate No. 2 = 10.75 x .1913 x .83910 = 1.725 in. or $1\frac{23}{32}$ in.

Ordinate No. 3 = 10.75 x .3535 x .83910 = 3.188 in. or $3\frac{3}{16}$ in.

Ordinate No. 4 = 10.75 x .4619 x .83910 = 4.166 in. or $4\frac{11}{64}$ in.

Ordinate No. 5 = 10.75 x .5000 x .83910 = 4.510 in. or $4\frac{33}{64}$ in.

1. To draw the center line of the fitting, place a wrap around on the pipe at the center of the turn. Using the wrap around as a guide, draw a straight line around the pipe with soapstone or chalk. (See Fig. 47.)

2. To divide the outside circumference of the pipe into 16 equal parts, first wrap a piece of paper around the pipe and tear off the part that over-

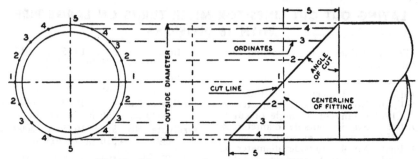

Fig. 58. Miter turn on large pipe with 16 divisions.

laps. (See Fig. 48.) Fold the paper four times to obtain 16 divisions. Then wrap the paper around the pipe on the center line of the fitting and mark the divisions on the pipe. Number these divisions as shown in Fig. 58 and draw straight lines through these points. These lines will be the ordinate lines.

3. Find the lengths of Numbers 2, 3, 4, and 5 ordinates using the above formulas.

4. Lay out these measurements on their respective ordinate lines as shown in Fig. 58.

5. Connect these points with a wrap around as explained in **Fig. 51** to establish the cut line.

TEES

Full-Size Tee

Laying Out the Header

1. Place a wrap around on the pipe at the center of the branch. Draw a straight line around the pipe with soapstone or chalk, using the wrap around as a guide.

2. Divide the center line into four equal parts. (See p. 74.) Then draw a straight line about 10 in. long on the pipe at each quarter mark. A piece of small angle iron will aid in making straight lines. Number these lines as shown in Fig. 59 (*B*)—line No. 3 on top, No. 4 on the bottom, and Nos. 1 and 2 on the sides.

3. Mark off with soapstone points *A* and *B* on line 3 on each side of the center line. The distance from *A* and *B* to the center line should be equal to one-half of the outside diameter of the branch.

Note: Points *C* will be located at the intersection of the center line and lines 1 and 2.

4. Place a wrap around on the pipe and line it up with point *A* and points *C* on lines 1 and 2. Connect these points with a chalk line. Then line up the wrap around with *C*, *B*, and *C* and connect these points with a chalk line.

Note: Sometimes a pointed cut at points *C* is not desired. For a rounded cut, locate points *D*. The distance from points *C* to points *D* should be equal to two times the thickness of the pipe wall. Then draw a chalk line freehand connecting points D with the lines from A and B.

Note: When cutting, make a radial cut; that is, point the cutting tip at all times to the center of the pipe. Then, bevel the edges to a 45° angle after the cut has been made.

Laying Out the Branch

1. Divide the surface of the branch into four equal parts near the end. (See p. 74.) Then draw a straight, 6-in. line from the end of the pipe at the quarter marks. Number these lines as shown in Fig. 59 (C) — No. 3 on top, No. 4 on the bottom and Nos. 1 and 2 on the sides.

2. Mark off with soapstone points A and B on lines 1 and 2. The dis-

tance from A and B to the end of the pipe should be equal to one-half of the outside diameter of the pipe, E.

3. Place the wrap around on the pipe and line it up with point A and points C on lines 3 and 4 at the end of the pipe. Connect these points with a chalk line. Then line up the wrap around with points C, B, and C and connect these points with a chalk line.

Note: If the header has a rounded cut at points D, the branch will require a rounded cut. For a rounded cut, locate points D. The distance from points C to points D should be equal to two times the thickness of the pipe wall. Then draw a chalk line freehand connecting points D with the lines from A and B.

Note: Make a radial cut but do not bevel the branch.

NOTE: X equals 2 times the thickness of the pipe wall.

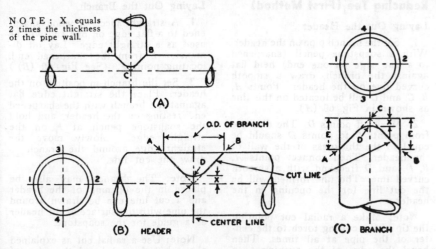

(A)

(B) HEADER

(C) BRANCH

Fig. 59. Full-size tee.

Reducing Tee (First Method)

Laying Out the Header

1. Set the branch pipe on the header. With a soapstone pencil (sharpened to a flat edge on one end) held flat against the branch, draw a smooth curved line on the header. Points A, B, C, and C will be located on this line as shown in Fig. 60 (*A*).

2. Mark off points D. The distance from points C to points D should be equal to the thickness of the wall of the header. Then connect points A, B, D, and D freehand with a smooth curved line. The line formed will be the cut line for the opening in the header.

Note: Make a radial cut pointing the tip of the cutting torch to the center of the pipe at all times. Then bevel the edge of the opening to a 45° angle.

Laying Out the Branch

1. A straight piece of wood sharpened to a flat edge on one end will be used as a straight edge. Lay off dimension E from the sharpened end, locating point F. (See Fig. 60 (*B*).)

2. Set the branch in position on the header. Place the straight edge flat against the branch with the sharpened end resting on the header, and hold the soapstone pencil at F on the straight edge. Slowly move the straight edge around the branch to draw the cut line.

Note: The branch may also be placed in the opening of the header and a cut line can be drawn around the pipe with the surface of the header as a guide for the soapstone.

Note: Use a radial cut as explained above but do not bevel the edge of the branch.

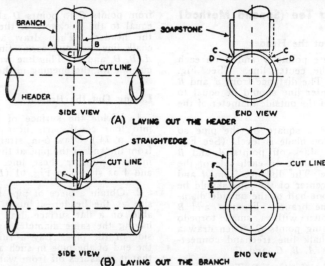

Fig. 60. Reducing tee (first method).

Reducing Tee (Second Method)

Laying Out the Header

1. Locate points A and B on each side of the center line. (See Fig. 61 (A).) The distance from A and B to the center line should be equal to one-half of the outside diameter of the branch.

2. Place a square on the pipe so that the top blade is level. (See Fig. 61 (B).) Mark off points A and B on the top blade on each side of the center line. The distance from A and B to the center of the pipe should be equal to one-half of the outside diameter of the branch. From A and B plumb down with a small torpedo level locating points C. Then draw a smooth chalk line freehand connecting points A, B, C, and C.

3. Mark off points D. The distance from points C to points D should be equal to the thickness of the wall of the header. Then draw a smooth chalk line freehand connecting points A, B, D, and D. This line will be the cut line for the opening in the header.

Laying Out the Branch

1. Divide the surface of the pipe into four equal parts near the end. (See p. 74.) Draw 6-in. straight lines from the end of the pipe at the quarter marks. Number these lines 1, 2, 3, and 4 as shown in Fig. 61 (D).

2. Obtain a piece of pipe the same size as the header—if none is available, on a flat surface draw a circle having the same diameter as the inside of the pipe. Lay a rule across the end of the pipe in such a manner that it measures off from wall to wall a distance equal to the outside diam-

4. Draw a smooth curved half line freehand connecting points A, C, B between the two final points 4 and cut. 5. Cut pipe. When pipe will be the cut line.

5. Cut pipe. Weld branch to the end of the branch to be welded to the header at points A, C, B. (See Fig. 61.)

Note: Points 1, 2, 3, 4 are the number of this pipe on these points [?]

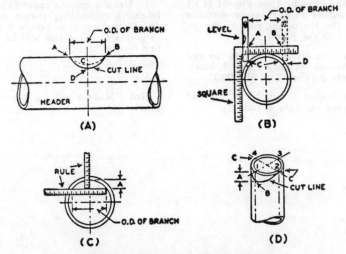

Fig. 61. Reducing tee (second method).

eter of the branch. (See Fig. 61 (*C*).) With another rule, measure distance *A* from the top of the rule to the inside wall of the pipe.

3. Lay out distance *A* from the end of the branch on lines 1 and 3, locating points *B*. (See Fig. 61 (*D*).)

Note: Points *C* will be at the end of the pipe on lines 4 and 2.

4. Draw a smooth curved chalk line freehand connecting points *B*, *C*, *B*, and *C*, turning in at points *B* and out at points *C*. This line will be the cut line for the branch.

Note: Make a radial cut and do not bevel.

LATERALS

Full-Size Lateral

Lay out a full-size view of the lateral on any smooth, flat surface as follows:

1. Lay out the two center lines for the angle of the branch needed. (The angle may be laid out by the method shown on p. 31.)

2. Lay out lines on each side of the center lines at a distance equal to one-half of the outside diameter of the pipe. These lines are to be parallel with the center lines. They will intersect at points *A* and *B*. (See Fig. 62 (*A*).)

3. Draw straight lines from points *A* and *B* to the intersection of the two center lines at point *C*. These lines will be the cut lines.

Laying Out the Header

1. Draw a center line around the header at the point where the two center lines intersect. (See Fig. 62 (*B*).)

2. Divide the center line into four equal parts. (See p. 74.) Draw a straight line on the pipe at each quarter mark—one on top, one on the bottom, and one on each side.

3. Measure distance *D* and *E* on the sketch. Lay off these measurements on each side of the center line on the top line of the pipe, locating points *A* and *B*.

Note: Points *C* will be on each side of the pipe at the intersection of the center line and the quarter lines.

4. Line up a wrap around with *C*, *A*, and *C*, and connect these points with a chalk line. Then connect points *C*, *B*, and *C* in a similar manner. The line formed will be the cut line.

Note: Make a miter cut with the cutting torch and bevel the edge of the opening.

Laying Out the Branch

1. Divide the surface of the pipe into four equal parts near the end. Draw straight lines from the end of the pipe at each quarter mark. Number these lines 1, 2, 3, and 4, as shown in Fig. 62 (*C*).

2. On the sketch at point *B* draw a line at right angles to the side of the branch to obtain distance *F*. (See Fig. 62 (*A*).) Then lay off distance *F* from the end of the branch pipe on

lines 1 and 2. Draw a straight chalk line around the pipe at these points. This line is the base line.

Note: Point *B* will be on line 4 at the intersection of the base line and line 4.

Measure distance *G* on the sketch. Then lay off distance *G* on the pipe from the base line on line 3, locating point *A*.

3. Line up the wrap around with *C*, *A*, and *C* and draw a chalk line connecting these three points. Then connect points *C*, *B*, and *C* with a chalk line. The line formed will be the cut line.

Note: Make a miter cut with the cutting torch and bevel the edge of the opening.

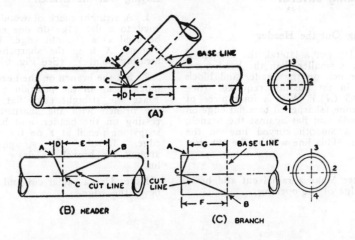

Fig. 62. Full-size lateral.

Reducing Lateral

Laying Out the Header

To lay out a lateral, the branch of which is smaller than the header, set the branch on the header and block it up in the position required. (See Fig. 63 (*A*).) With a long piece of soapstone (sharpened to a flat edge on one end) laid flat against the branch, draw a smooth curved line on the header. This line will be the cut line.

Note: Make a radial cut and bevel the edge of the opening.

Laying Out the Branch

1. A straight piece of wood sharpened to a flat edge on one end will be used as a straight edge. Lay off distance *X* from the sharpened end, locating point *Y*. (See Fig. 63 (*B*).)

2. Set the branch on the header and block it up in the position required. Place the straight edge flat against the branch with the sharpened end resting on the header, and hold the soapstone pencil at *Y* on the straight edge. Revolve the straight edge around the branch to draw the cut line.

Note: Use a radial cut and do not bevel the edge.

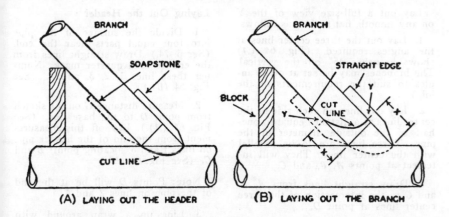

(A) LAYING OUT THE HEADER   (B) LAYING OUT THE BRANCH

Fig. 63. Reducing lateral.

TRUE Y

Lay out a full-size view of the Y on any smooth, flat surface as follows:

1. Lay out the three center lines at the angles required. (Fig. 64 (*A*) shows branches 45° off the vertical. The branches may be set at other angles to suit the requirements of the job.)

2. Lay out lines on each side of the center lines at a distance equal to one-half of the outside diameter of the pipe. These lines are to be parallel with the center lines. They will intersect at points *A*, *B*, and *C*.

3. Draw straight lines from *A*, *B*, and *C* to the intersection of the three center lines at point *D*.

4. Draw the base lines, indicated by the dotted lines, at right angles to the center lines.

Laying Out the Header

1. Divide the surface of the pipe into four equal parts near the end. (See p. 74.) Draw straight lines from the end at each quarter mark. Number these lines 1, 2, 3, and 4. (See Fig. 64 (*B*).)

2. Measure distance *G* on the sketch from point *D* to the base line. (See Fig. 64 (*A*).) Lay off this measurement from the end of the header pipe on lines 1 and 3, locating points *B* and *C*. (See Fig. 64 (*B*).)

Note: Points *D* will be at the end of the pipe on lines 2 and 4.

3. Line up a wrap around with points *D*, *B*, and *D* and connect these points with a chalk line. Then connect points *D*, *C*, and *D* with a chalk

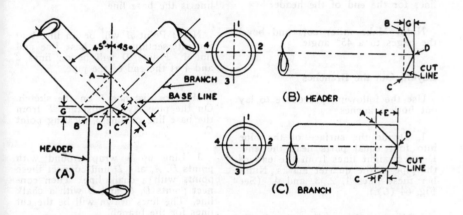

Fig. 64. True Y.

line. The lines drawn will be the cut lines for the end of the header.

Note: Make miter cuts and bevel the edges to a 45° angle.

Laying Out the Branches

Use the following procedure to lay out both branches:

1. Divide the surface of the pipe into four equal parts near the end. Draw straight lines from the end of the pipe at the quarter marks. Number these lines 1, 2, 3, and 4. (See Fig. 64 (*C*).)

2. Measure distance *E* on the sketch. (See Fig. 64 (*A*).) Lay off distance *E* from the end of the branch pipe on lines 2 and 4. Draw a straight line

around the pipe at these points. This line is the base line.

Note: Point *A* will be on line 1 at the intersection of the base line and line 1. Points *D* will be on lines 2 and 4 at the end of the pipe.

Measure distance *F* on the sketch. On the pipe lay off distance *F* from the base line on line 3, locating point *C*.

3. Line up a wrap around with points *D*, *A*, and *D* and connect these points with a chalk line. Then connect points *D*, *C*, and *D* with a chalk line. The lines drawn will be the cut lines for the branch.

Note: Make a miter cut and bevel the edges to a 45° angle.

REDUCERS

A reducer is a pipe alteration which accommodates a larger pipe to one of a smaller diameter.

Concentric Reducer

With a concentric reducer, the center line of the larger pipe is in line with the center line of the smaller pipe. (See Fig. 65 (B).) Use the following procedure to lay out a concentric reducer:

1. From the table on pages 105-106 determine the number of arms for the size of pipe to be reduced. Divide the outside surface of the pipe near the end into the number of parts equal to the number of arms. Then draw lines from the end at the division points. These lines are reference lines.

2. Measure off distance C (see the table on pp. 105-106 from the end of

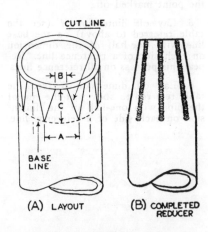

(A) LAYOUT   (B) COMPLETED
                      REDUCER

Fig. 65. Concentric reducer.

the pipe. (See Fig. 65 (*A*).) Then draw the base line around the pipe at the point marked off.

3. Lay off dimension *A* (see the table referred to above) on the base line with one-half of the dimension on each side of a reference line. Repeat this process on all reference lines.

4. Lay off dimension *B* (see the table referred to above) at the end of the pipe with one-half of the dimension on each side of a reference line.

Repeat this process on all reference lines.

5. Connect the points marked off with straight lines as shown in Fig. 65 (*A*). These lines will be the cut lines.

Note: When cutting, point the tip of the torch to the center of the pipe at all times. Bevel each arm to a 45° angle. Heat each arm on the base line and bend it into position.

CONCENTRIC-REDUCER DATA

Size, in Inches	No. of Arms	A, in Inches	B, in Inches	C, in Inches
3 x2½	4	2¾	2¼	3
3 x2	4	2¾	1⅞	3
3 x1½	4	2¾	1½	3
3 x1¼	4	2¾	1 5/16	3
3 x1	4	2¾	1 1/16	3
3½x3	4	3⅛	2¾	3
3½x2½	4	3⅛	2¼	3
3½x2	4	3⅛	1⅞	3
3½x1½	4	3⅛	1½	3½
3½x1¼	4	3⅛	1 5/16	3½
3½x1	4	3⅛	1 1/16	3½
4 x3½	4	3½	3⅛	3
4 x3	4	3½	2¾	3
4 x2½	4	3½	2¼	3
4 x2	4	3½	1⅞	3
4 x1½	4	3½	1½	3½
4 x1¼	4	3½	1 5/16	3¾
4 x1	4	3½	1 1/16	4¼
5 x4	4	4⅜	3½	4
5 x3½	4	4⅜	3⅛	4
5 x3	4	4⅜	2¾	4
5 x2½	4	4⅜	2¼	4
5 x2	5	3½	1½	4
5 x1½	5	3½	1 3/16	4¾
5 x1¼	5	3½	1 1/16	5
5 x1	6	2 15/16	11/16	5½
6 x5	5	4 5/32	3 17/32	4
6 x4	5	4 5/32	2 13/16	4
6 x3½	5	4 5/32	2½	4
6 x3	5	4 5/32	2 7/32	4
6 x2½	5	4 5/32	1 13/16	5
6 x2	6	3 15/32	1¼	5½
6 x1½	6	3 15/32	1	6

CONCENTRIC-REDUCER DATA (Cont'd)

Size, in Inches	No. of Arms	A, in Inches	B, in Inches	C, in Inches
6x1¼	7	2 31/32	¾	6½
6x1	7	2 31/32	9/16	7
8x6	6	4½	3 15/32	4
8x5	6	4½	2 29/32	4
8x4	6	4½	2 11/32	5½
8x3½	6	4½	2 3/32	6
8x3	7	3⅞	1 9/16	6½
8x2½	8	3⅜	1⅛	7½
8x2	8	3⅜	15/16	8¼
8x1½	9	3	21/32	8½
8x1¼	9	3	9/16	9
10x8	7	4 13/16	3⅞	4
10x6	7	4 13/16	3	5½
10x5	7	4 13/16	2½	6½
10x4	8	4¼	1¾	8¼
10x3½	9	3¾	1⅜	9
10x3	10	3⅜	1⅛	9½
10x2½	11	3 1/16	¾	10¼
10x2	11	3 1/16	11/16	11
10x1½	12	2 13/16	½	11½
12x10	8	5	4 7/32	4
12x8	10	4	2 11/16	5¼
12x6	10	4	2 1/16	8
12x5	10	4	1¾	9¼
12x4	11	3¾	1 7/16	10¾
12x3½	12	3 5/16	1 1/16	11½
12x3	12	3 5/16	15/16	12
12x2½	12	3 5/16	¾	13
12x2	12	3 5/16	⅝	13½

Eccentric Reducer

With an eccentric reducer the center line of the larger pipe is out of line with the center line of the smaller pipe. (See Fig. 66 (C).) Use the following procedure to lay out an eccentric reducer:

1. Measure off distance E ($1\frac{1}{2}$ times the diameter of the larger pipe) from the end of the pipe. (See Fig. 66 (A).) Then draw line Y-Z around the pipe at the point marked off.

2. Divide the outside surface of the pipe into eight equal parts, starting at the top of the pipe. Then draw straight lines from the end of the pipe to line Y-Z at these eight points. Number these reference lines at the intersection of Y-Z as follows: 7, 8, 9, 10, and 11.

3. For a 30° slope, multiply dimension E by the constant .866 and lay out this distance on the bottom reference line, locating point X.

4. Lay off a dimension equal to $\frac{3}{8}$ of the circumference of the smaller pipe at X with one-half of the dimension on each side of the bottom reference line, locating points 1. Connect points 1, X, and 1 with a straight line.

5. Line up a wrap around with points 1 and the top reference line at the end of the pipe and draw a chalk line. As a result, the length of each reference line will vary.

Note: The following steps will complete the layout of one-half the pipe. The other half is completed exactly the same way.

6. At the end of the pipe lay out dimension A with one-half of the di-

mension on each side of the top reference line, locating points 6. (See Fig. 66 (*B*).) For dimensions, see note on p. 109.

7. From point 6, lay out dimensions *B*, *A*, *C*, *A*, and *D* down to point 1. Then project points 2, 3, 4, and 5 back from the end of the pipe to the sloping line.

8. Draw a line parallel with the end of the pipe from point 5 to 4. Similarly connect points 3 and 2. Then using a wrap around as a guide, draw straight lines from points 6 and 5 to point 10. Similarly connect points 4, 9, and 3 and points 2, 8, and 1. The lines drawn will be the cut lines for the eccentric reducer.

Note: After the arms have been cut, bevel the edges. The arms are now ready to be bent. First, heat the bottom piece and bend it into shape to correspond to the curvature of the smaller pipe. Then heat the top arm on line *Y-Z* and bend it into position. Then bend the other arms into position and trim the ends as desired.

As an aid in forming the arms to the correct size, use a piece of pipe with an outside diameter about equal to the inside diameter of the smaller pipe.

Note: The eccentric may be lengthened or shortened to suit the requirements of the job.

Note: To find the outside circumference of a pipe, multiply the outside diameter of the pipe by 3.1416 and add ⅛ of an inch, as most pipes are slightly oversize.

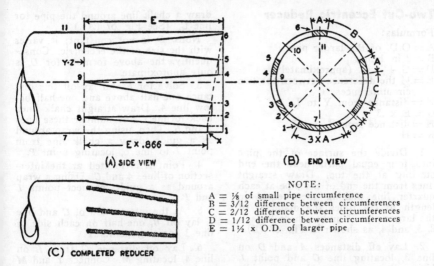

(A) SIDE VIEW

(B) END VIEW

(C) COMPLETED REDUCER

NOTE:
A = ⅛ of small pipe circumference
B = 3/12 difference between circumferences
C = 2/12 difference between circumferences
D = 1/12 difference between circumferences
E = 1½ x O.D. of larger pipe

Fig. 66. Eccentric reducer.

Two-Cut Eccentric Reducer

Formulas:

A = O.D. of the larger pipe
B = 2 in. hinge
D = G + 1 in. (approximately)
E = ½ the difference between the two circumferences
F = distance from Y to L
G = E x .3
H = distance from L to P
K = H

1. Divide the surface of the pipe into four equal parts near the end starting at the top. Draw straight lines from the end of the pipe at each quarter line making them equal in length to 1½ times the diameter of the larger pipe. Number these lines 1, 2, 3, and 4, as shown in Fig. 67 (B).

2. Lay off distances A and D on line 3, locating line C and point J. Using the wrap around as a guide,

draw a chalk line around the pipe for line C. (See Fig. 67 (A).)

Note: D is not constant; it varies with the size of the eccentric. Consequently, the above formula for D is only approximate.

3. Solve for E and lay off this distance one-half above and one-half below line 4. Draw straight chalk lines back to line C and number these lines 5 and 6. Then, using the wrap around as a guide, draw a chalk line from point J to line 6, locating point P.

4. Point L is located at the intersection of lines 4 and C. Using a wrap around as a guide, connect points L and P.

5. At the intersection of C and line 1, lay off B, one-half on each side of line 1 locating points Y.

6. Lay off distance G from L on line 4, locating M. Connect Y and M with a straight chalk line.

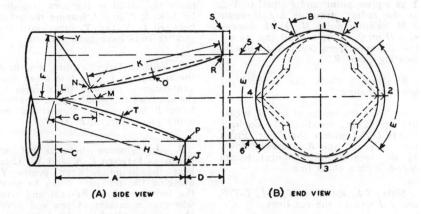

Fig. 67. Two-cut eccentric reducer.

7. With the wrap around and using *Y* as a pivot point, and *F* equal to *Y-L* as the radius, draw an arc through *Y-M* locating point *N*. Mark dimension *H* on the wrap around and lay off this distance from point *N* to line 5, locating point *R*.

8. Draw a chalk line from *R* to line 1, locating *S*.

9. From the center of line *H*, measure up ¼ in., locating *T*. Connect points *L-T-P* with a chalk line. From the center of line *K*, measure down ¼ in., locating *O*. Connect points *N-O-R* with a chalk line.

Note: *S-R, R-O-N, N-Y, Y-L, L-T-P,* and *P-J* will be the cut lines.

10. Lay off these points on the other side of the pipe to complete the eccentric.

Note: 1. With a cutting torch, remove the metal in the area bounded by *S, R, L, P,* and *J*, leaving the areas between *L, N,* and *Y* uncut until the smaller ends have been formed.

2. With a large welding tip, heat the areas from *J, P,* to *L* to a red heat and hammer them in to conform to the shape of the smaller pipe, tapering from *P* back to *L*. Repeat on the upper piece from *S, R,* to *N*.

3. After shaping the ends, cut out the areas between *L, N,* and *Y*. Then heat the hinge between points *Y*, bringing the top part down to meet the lower portion. Re-heat and trim wherever necessary. Open and bevel the edges. Re-heat the hinge and bring the top portion into position and the eccentric is prepared for welding.

METHODS OF BLANKING OFF PIPE

Orange Peel

The orange peel (Fig. 68 (*C*)) is one method of blanking off the end of a pipe. The orange peel may be used for any size of pipe or any amount of pressure.

1. From the table on page 114, determine the number of arms for the size of the pipe. Divide the outside surface of the pipe near the end into the number of parts equal to the number of arms. Then draw lines back from the end of the pipe at these division points. These lines are reference lines.

2. Measure off distance *A* (see the table referred to above) from the end of the pipe. Then draw the base line around the pipe at the point marked off. (See Fig. 68 (*B*).)

3. Draw a template for one arm on a piece of paper as shown in Fig. 68 (*A*) as follows:

a. Draw a straight line equal in length to dimension *A*.

b. Divide the line into three equal parts.

c. Draw lines on these three points at right angles to the center line.

d. Obtain dimensions *E*, *B*, and *C* from the table referred to above and lay them off on lines *X*, *Y*, and *Z*.

e. Connect the ends of these lines and point *F* with straight lines.

f. Cut out the template with a knife or scissors.

4. Place the template on the pipe, lining up the center line of the template with one of the reference lines. Then mark around the template with soapstone to lay out one arm. Repeat this process on all reference lines to lay out the arms necessary to make the complete orange peel.

Note: When cutting, use a radial cut; that is, point the tip of the torch to the center of the pipe at all times Bevel the edges of all arms to a 45° angle. Then, heat the arms and bend them to shape.

ORANGE-PEEL DATA

Pipe size, in Inches	No. of Arms	A, in Inches	B, in Inches	C, in Inches	E, in Inches
1½	4	1½	1½	1 5/16	¾
2	4	1⅞	1⅞	1⅝	15/16
2½	4	2¼	2¼	1 31/32	1⅛
3	4	2¾	2¾	2 13/32	1⅜
3½	4	3⅛	3⅛	2¾	1 9/16
4	4	3½	3 17/32	3 1/16	1¾
5	5	4⅜	3½	3 1/16	1¾
6	5	5¼	4⅛	3⅝	2 1/16
8	5	6¾	5⅜	4¾	2 11/16
10	7	8½	4 13/16	4¼	2⅜
12	8	10	5	4⅜	2½

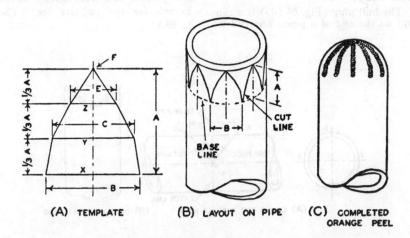

(A) TEMPLATE   (B) LAYOUT ON PIPE   (C) COMPLETED
                                                  ORANGE PEEL

Fig. 68. Orange peel.

Bull Plug

The bull plug (Fig. 69 (B)) is a cap put on the end of a pipe. The end of the pipe is laid out exactly as the branch for the full-size tee. (See p. 88.)

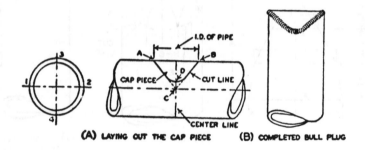

(A) LAYING OUT THE CAP PIECE   (B) COMPLETED BULL PLUG

Fig. 69. Bull plug.

Laying Out the Cap Piece

1. On a piece of pipe the same size as the pipe to be capped, lay out a center line. (See Fig. 69 (*A*).)

2. Divide the center line into four equal parts starting at the top of the pipe. (See p. 74.) Then draw a straight line on the pipe at each quarter mark. Number these lines as follows: No. 3 on top, No. 4 on the bottom, and Nos. 1 and 2 on the sides.

3. Mark off points *A* and *B* on line 3 on each side of the center line. The distance from *A* and *B* to the center line should be equal to one-half of the inside diameter of the pipe.

Note: Points *C* will be at the intersection of the center line and lines 1 and 2.

4. Line up a wrap around with points *C*, *A*, and *C* and draw a chalk line connecting these points. Then connect points *C*, *B*, and *C*.

5. Mark off point *D* on both sides of the pipe. The distance from *C* to *D* should be equal to two times the thickness of the pipe wall.

6. Draw a curved, freehand line connecting points *A*, *B*, *D*, and *D*. This line will be the cut line.

Note: Use a radial cut when cutting out the cap piece.

Laying Out the End of the Pipe

1. Divide the outer surface of the pipe into four equal parts at the end of the pipe. Draw straight lines from the end of the pipe on each of the quarter marks. Number each line from 1 to 4 as shown in Fig. 70.

2. Observe that dimension *E* equals one-half the outside diameter of the pipe. On lines 3 and 4, measure dimension *E* from the end of the pipe locating points *F*. Point *H* will be located at the end of the pipe on line 1. Point *J* will be located at the end of the pipe on line 2.

3. Line up a wrap around with points *F*, *H*, and *F*. Connect these 3 points with a chalk line. Connect points *F*, *J*, and *F* the same way.

4. On line 3 locate point *G*. The distance from *F* to *G* will be equal to two tmes the pipe-wall thickness. Connect point *G* with lines *F-H* and *J-F* with a smooth, freehand curved line. Repeat on the opposite side of the pipe on line 4.

Note: Use a radial cut when cutting the end of the pipe and bevel wherever necessary.

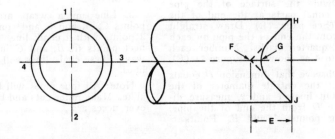

Fig. 70. Laying out the end of the pipe for a bull plug.

FULL-SIZE CROSS

Laying Out the Cut Lines

1. Divide the surface of the pipe into 4 equal parts at the end of the pipe. (See page 74.) Draw straight lines from the end of the pipe on each of the quarter marks. Number each line 1 to 4 as shown in Figure 71 (*B*).

2. Observe that dimension *D* equals one-half the outside diameter of the pipe. On lines 1 and 2, measure dimension *D* from the end of the pipe, locating points *A* and *B*. Points *C*

will be located on lines 3 and 4 at end of pipe.

3. Line up a wrap around with points *C*, *A*, and *C* and connect these 3 points with a chalk line. Then connect points *C*, *B*, and *C* in the same way. These chalk lines will be the cut lines.

Note: All four pipes will be laid out alike. Make miter cuts and bevel wherever necessary.

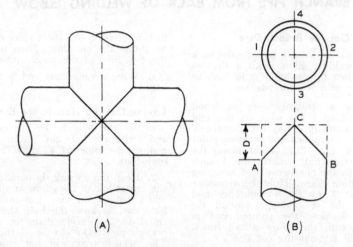

Fig. 71. Full-size cross.

BRANCH PIPE FROM BACK OF WELDING ELBOW

Laying Out the Branch Pipe

1. Tack the branch pipe on the back of the welding elbow with a shallow tack. Then tack a brace onto both to hold the members in position.

2. Use a straight piece of wood sharpened to a flat edge on one end as a straightedge. Lay off distance X from the sharpened end locating point Y. (See Fig. 72.) Then place the straightedge flat against the branch pipe with the sharpened end touching the welding elbow. Hold the soapstone pencil at Y on the straightedge and revolve the straightedge around the branch, keeping the pointed end in contact with the elbow at all times. This will lay out the cut line.

3. If the branch pipe is too long to

tack in place, use a short piece of pipe to obtain the cut line. Then transfer the cut lines to the longer pipe.

4. Make a radial cut and bevel the edge.

Laying Out the Hole in the Elbow

1. Set the branch pipe in position and scribe the hole cut line using the end of the pipe as a guide for the soapstone.

2. Keep the cutting tip parallel with the center line of the elbow at all times when making the cut. Cut inside the hole line, because the hole should be equal to the inside diameter of the branch pipe. Do not bevel the hole. The branch pipe will not enter the hole.

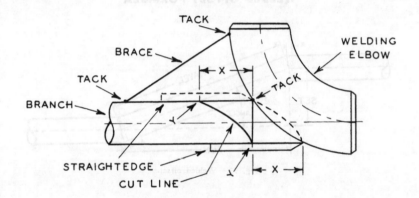

Fig. 72. Branch pipe from back of welding elbow.

WELDED OFFSET FORMULA

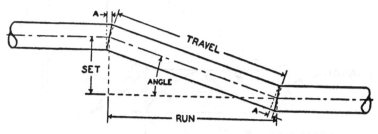

Fig. 73. Welded offset.

Angle of cut = one-half of angle of turn
A = measure-back distance = O.D. of
    pipe x tangent of angle of cut*
Travel = set x cosecant of angle of
    turn

Run = set x cotangent of angle of
    turn

* See the Trigonometry Table, pages 190 to
194, for constants, i.e., the values of the
cosecants, and cotangents.

WELDED ROLLING OFFSETS

Formula:

$$A = \sqrt{roll^2 + set^2}$$

Angle B = A ÷ advance = tangent of angle B

Length of travel piece c. to c. = cosecant of angle B x distance A

Example:

Lay out a welded rolling offset (see Fig. 74) given the following dimensions: roll 10 in., set 24 in., advance 36 in., diameter of pipe 4 in.

1. Find the angle of cut.

$$A = \sqrt{roll^2 + set^2}$$
$$A = \sqrt{10^2 + 24^2} = \sqrt{100 + 576} = \sqrt{676} = 26 \text{ in.}$$

Tangent of angle B = A ÷ advance
Tangent of angle B = 26 ÷ 36 = .72222

Angle B = 36° (See the Trigonometry Table, pp. 190–194.)

Angle of cut = 36 ÷ 2 = 18°

2. Find the length of the travel piece.

Length of travel piece = cosecant of angle B x distance A

Length of travel piece = cosecant of 36° x 26 = 1.7013 x 26 = 44.233 in. or 44¼ in. (See the Trigonometry Table.)

3. Lay out the cut lines on the travel piece. (See pp. 78-79.)

4. Locate point *X* on the runs.

Note: The center lines of the cuts on the runs must be located at *X*, an arc of *F* inches (see Fig. 74) from the top center of the pipe to produce the

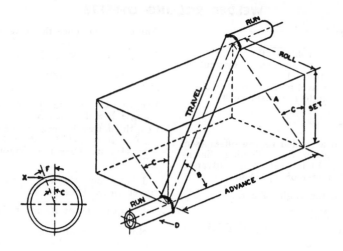

Fig. 74. Welded rolling offset.

required roll. The number of degrees of roll is equal to angle C.

a. Find angle C.
   Cotangent of angle C = set ÷ roll
   Cotangent of angle C = 24/10 = 2.4000
   Angle C = 22½° (See Trigonometry Table.)

b. Find the length of arc F.
   Arc F = radius x angle C x .01745
   Arc F = 2.25 in.* x 22.5° x .01745 — ⅞ in.

c. Lay off arc F from the top center of the pipe, locating point X, the center line of the cut.

5. Lay out the quarter lines on the runs from point X. Then lay out the cut lines on the runs.

---

*The outside diameter of 4-in. pipe is 4½ in. The radius is one-half of the O.D. or 4½ ÷ 2 = 2¼ in.

ANGLE IRON BRACKETS

For the values in the following formulas, see Fig. 75.

30° x 60° Angle Iron Brackets

Formulas:

$A = B$ x .577
$B = A$ x 1.732
$C = A$ x 2.000
$C = B$ x 1.155
$D =$ width of angle iron
$E = D$ x 3.732 for a three-piece bracket
$E = G$ x 3.732 for a one-piece bracket
$F = D$ x 1.732
$G = D$ — thickness of metal

Example for a Three Piece Bracket:

Determine the necessary dimensions for a three piece 30° x 60° angle iron bracket, if dimension A is 18 in. and the width of the angle iron is 2 in.

$A = 18$ in.
$B = 18$ x 1.732 $= 31.176$ in. or 2 ft. 7³⁄₁₆ in.
$C = 18$ x 2.000 $= 36$ in. or 3 ft.
$D = 2$ in.
$E = 2$ x 3.732 $= 7.464$ in. or 7¹⁵⁄₃₂ in.
$F = 2$ x 1.732 $= 3.464$ in. or 3¹⁵⁄₃₂ in.

Example for a One-Piece Bracket

Lay out the above bracket in one piece. The thickness of the metal is ¼ in.

$A = 18$ in.
$B = 18$ x 1.732 $= 31.176$ in. or 2 ft. 7³⁄₁₆ in.
$C = 18$ x 2.000 $= 36$ in. or 3 ft.
$D = 2$ in.
$E = 1.75$ x 3.732 $= 6.531$ in. or 6¹⁷⁄₃₂ in.
$F = 2$ x 1.732 $= 3.464$ or 3¹⁵⁄₃₂ in.
$G = 2 — .25 = 1.75$ in. or 1¾ in.

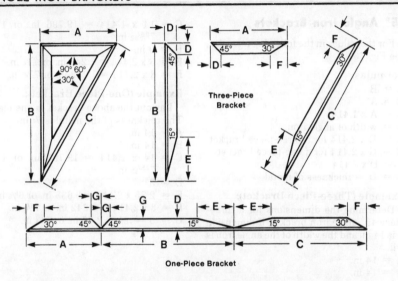

Fig. 75. 30° x 60° angle iron brackets.

45° Angle Iron Brackets

For the values in the following formulas, see Fig. 76.

Formulas:
A = B
B = A
C = A x 1.414
D = width of angle iron
E = D x 2.414 for a three-piece bracket
E = G x 2.414 for a one-piece bracket
F = D x 2.414
G = D — thickness of metal

Example (Three-Piece Bracket):

Determine the dimensions for a three-piece 45° angle iron bracket, if dimension A is 14 in. and the width of the angle iron is 3 in.

A = 14 in.
B = 14 in.
C = 14 x 1.414 = 19.796 in. or 1 ft. 7^{25}/$_{32}$ in.
D = 3 in.
E = 3 x 2.414 = 7.242 in. or 7$\frac{1}{4}$ in.
F = 3 x 2.414 = 7.242 in. or 7$\frac{1}{4}$ in.

Example (One-Piece Bracket):

Lay out the above bracket in one piece. The thickness of the metal is $\frac{1}{4}$ in.

A = 14 in.
B = 14 in.
C = 14 x 1.414 = 19.796 in. or 1 ft. 7^{25}/$_{32}$ in.
D = 3
E = 2.75 x 2.414 = 6.638 in. or 6$\frac{5}{8}$ in.
F = 3 x 2.414 = 7.242 in. or 7$\frac{1}{4}$ in.
G = 3 — .25 = 2.75 in. or 2$\frac{3}{4}$ in.

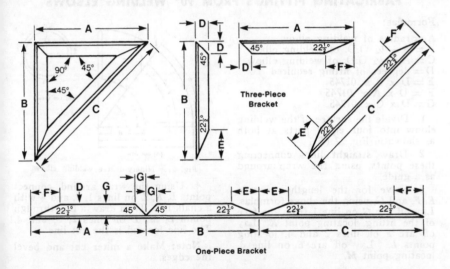

Fig. 76. 45° angle iron brackets.

FABRICATING FITTINGS FROM 90° WELDING ELBOWS

Formulas:

A = radius of welding elbow
B = A — ½ O.D. of welding elbow
C = A + ½ O.D. of welding elbow
D = degrees of fitting required
E = D x B x .01745
F = D x A x .01745
G = D x C x .01745

1. Divide the surface of the welding elbow into four equal parts at both as shown in Fig. 77 (B).

2. Draw straight lines connecting these points, using the wrap around as a guide.

3. Solve for the lengths of arcs E, F, and G, using the above formulas. Lay off arc G on line 1 from the face of the fitting, locating point K. Lay off arc F on lines 2 and 4, locating points L. Lay off arc E on line 3, locating point M.

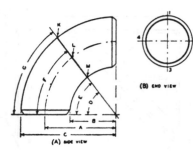

Fig. 77. Ninety-degree welding elbow.

4. Using the wrap around, connect points L, K, L on lines 1, 2, and 4 with a chalk line. Then draw a line through points L, M, L on lines 2, 3, and 4. The line formed is the cut line.

Note: Make a miter cut and bevel the edges.

4

REFERENCE TABLES

STANDARD CAST-IRON SCREWED FITTINGS

Pipe Sizes, in Inches	Dimensions in Inches					
	A	B	C	D	E	F
¼	.812	.750				.312
⅜	.937	.812				.375
½	1.125	.875	.750	2.500	1.875	.437
¾	1.312	1.000	.875	3.000	2.125	.500
1	1.437	1.125	1.000	3.500	2.750	.562
1¼	1.750	1.312	1.125	4.250	3.250	.562
1½	1.937	1.437	1.250	4.875	3.812	.562
2	2.250	1.687	1.437	5.750	4.500	.625
2½	2.687	1.937	1.562	6.750	5.187	.875
3	3.125	2.187	1.750	7.875	6.125	1.000
3½	3.437	2.375		8.875	6.875	1.062
4	3.750	2.625	2.062	9.750	7.625	1.062
5	4.437	3.062	2.250	11.625	9.250	1.187
6	5.125	3.437	2.437	13.437	10.750	1.187
8	6.500	4.250		16.937	13.625	1.312
10	7.875	5.187		20.687	16.750	1.500
12	9.250	6.000		24.125	19.625	1.625

Note: To change decimals to fractions, see the decimal equivalent table, page 178.

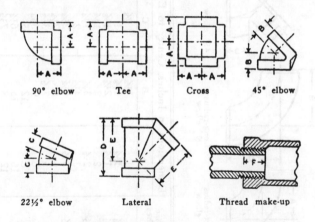

90° elbow   Tee   Cross   45° elbow

22½° elbow   Lateral   Thread make-up

Standard Cast-Iron Screwed Fittings.

STEEL BUTT-WELDING FITTINGS
(Standard and Extra Heavy)

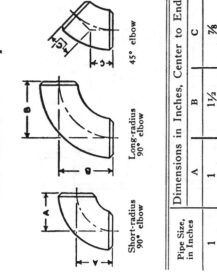

45° elbow

Long-radius 90° elbow

Short-radius 90° elbow

Pipe Size, in Inches	Dimensions in Inches, Center to End		
	A	B	C
1	1	1½	⅞
1¼	1¼	1⅞	1
1½	1½	2¼	1⅛
2	2	3	1⅜
2½	2½	3¾	1¾
3	3	4½	2
3½	3½	5¼	2¼
4	4	6	2½
5	5	7½	3⅛
6	6	9	3¾
8	8	12	5
10	10	15	6¼
12	12	18	7½

STEEL BUTT-WELDING FITTINGS (Cont'd)
(Standard and Extra Heavy)

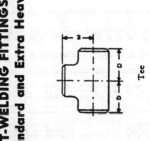

Tee

Pipe Size, in Inches	Dimensions in Inches, Center to End	
	D	E
1	1½	1½
1¼	1⅞	1⅞
1½	2¼	2¼
2	2½	2½
2½	3	3
3	3⅜	3⅜
3½	3¾	3¾
4	4⅛	4⅛
5	4⅞	4⅞
6	5⅝	5⅝
8	7	7
10	8½	8½
12	10	10

STEEL BUTT-WELDING FITTINGS (Cont'd) (Standard and Extra Heavy)

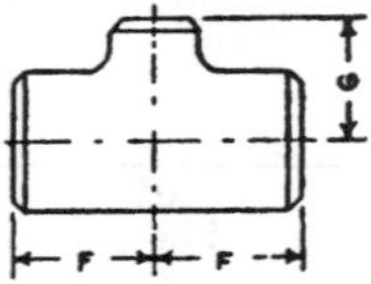

Reducing tee

Pipe Size, in Inches	Dimensions in Inches, Center to End F	Dimensions in Inches, Center to End G	Pipe Size, in Inches	Dimensions in Inches, Center to End F	Dimensions in Inches, Center to End G
1 x½	1½	1½	3½x2½	3¾	3½
1 x¾	1½	1½	3½x3	3¾	3⅝
1¼x½	1⅞	1⅞	4 x1½	4⅛	3⅜
1¼x¾	1⅞	1⅞	4 x2	4⅛	3½
1¼x1	1⅞	1⅞	4 x2½	4⅛	3¾
			4 x3	4⅛	3⅞
1½x½	2¼	2¼	4 x3½	4⅛	4
1½x¾	2¼	2¼			
1½x1	2¼	2¼	5 x2	4⅞	4⅛
1½x1¼	2¼	2¼	5 x2½	4⅞	4¼
			5 x3	4⅞	4⅜
2 x¾	2½	1¾	5 x3½	4⅞	4½
2 x1	2½	2	5 x4	4⅞	4⅝
2 x1¼	2½	2¼			
2 x1½	2½	2⅜	6 x2½	5⅝	4¾
			6 x3	5⅝	4⅞
2½x1	3	2¼	6 x3½	5⅝	5
2½x1¼	3	2½	6 x4	5⅝	5⅛
2½x1½	3	2⅝	6 x5	5⅝	5⅜
2½x2	3	2¾			
			8 x3	7	6
3 x1	3⅜	2⅝	8 x3½	7	6
3 x1¼	3⅜	2¾	8 x4	7	6⅛
3 x1½	3⅜	2⅞	8 x5	7	6⅜
3 x2	3⅜	3	8 x6	7	6⅝
3 x2½	3⅜	3¼			
3½x1½	3¾	3⅛	10 x4	8½	7¼
3½x2	3¾	3¼	10 x5	8½	7½

STEEL BUTT-WELDING FITTINGS (Cont'd)
(Standard and Extra Heavy)
REDUCING TEES (Cont'd)

Pipe Size, in Inches	Dimensions in Inches, Center to End	
	F	G
10x6	8½	7⅝
10x8	8½	8
12x5	10	8½

Pipe Size, in Inches	Dimensions in Inches, Center to End	
	F	G
12x6	10	8⅝
12x8	10	9
12x10	10	9½

STEEL BUTT-WELDING FITTINGS (Cont'd)
(Standard and Extra Heavy)

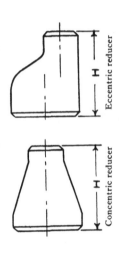

Concentric reducer

Eccentric reducer

Pipe Size, in Inches	H, in Inches	Pipe Size, in Inches	H, in Inches
1 x1/2	2	3 1/2 x1 1/4	4
1 x3/4	2	3 1/2 x1 1/2	4
1 1/4 x1/2	2	3 1/2 x2	4
1 1/4 x3/4	2	3 1/2 x2 1/2	4
1 1/4 x1	2	3 1/2 x3	4
1 1/2 x1/2	2 1/2	4 x1 1/2	4
1 1/2 x3/4	2 1/2	4 x2	4
1 1/2 x1	2 1/2	4 x2 1/2	4
1 1/2 x1 1/4	2 1/2	4 x3	4
2 x3/4	3	4 x3 1/2	4
2 x1	3	5 x2	5
2 x1 1/4	3	5 x2 1/2	5
2 x1 1/2	3	5 x3	5
2 1/2 x1	3 1/2	5 x3 1/2	5
2 1/2 x1 1/4	3 1/2	5 x4	5
2 1/2 x1 1/2	3 1/2	6 x2 1/2	5 1/2
2 1/2 x2	3 1/2	6 x3	5 1/2
3 x1 1/4	3 1/2	6 x3 1/2	5 1/2
3 x1 1/2	3 1/2	6 x4	5 1/2
3 x2	3 1/2	6 x5	5 1/2
3 x2 1/2	3 1/2	8 x3 1/2	6

REDUCERS (Cont'd)

Pipe Size, in Inches	H, in Inches	Pipe Size, in Inches	H, in Inches
8x4	6	10x8	7
8x5	6	12x5	8
8x6	6	12x6	8
10x4	7	12x8	8
10x5	7	12x10	8
10x6	7		

RING GASKETS FOR COMPANION FLANGES

Pipe Size	Standard I.D. x O.D. in Inches	Extra Heavy I.D. x O.D. in Inches
1/2	1/2 x 1 7/8	1/2 x 2 1/8
3/4	3/4 x 2 1/4	3/4 x 2 5/8
1	1 x 2 5/8	1 x 2 7/8
1 1/4	1 1/4 x 3	1 1/4 x 3 1/4
1 1/2	1 1/2 x 3 3/8	1 1/2 x 3 3/4
2	2 x 4 1/8	2 x 4 3/8
2 1/2	2 1/2 x 4 7/8	2 1/2 x 5 1/8
3	3 x 5 3/8	3 x 5 7/8
3 1/2	3 1/2 x 6 3/8	3 1/2 x 6 1/2
4	4 x 6 7/8	4 x 7 1/8
5	5 x 7 3/4	5 x 8 1/2
6	6 x 8 3/4	6 x 9 7/8
8	8 x 11	8 x 12 1/8
10	10 x 13 3/8	10 x 14 1/4
12	12 x 16 1/8	12 x 16 5/8
14	13 3/4 x 17 3/4	13 3/4 x 19 1/8
16	15 3/4 x 20 1/4	15 3/4 x 21 1/4
18	17 1/4 x 21 5/8	17 x 23 1/2
20	19 1/4 x 23 7/8	19 x 25 3/4
24	23 3/4 x 28 1/4	23 x 30 1/2

CAST IRON FLANGED FITTINGS
125 Pound Cast Iron Flanged Fittings

Size	Dimensions in Inches					
	A	B	C	D	E	F
2	4½	6½	2½	8	2½	10½
2½	5	7	3	9½	2½	12
3	5½	7¾	3	10	3·	13
3½	6	8½	3½			
4	6½	9	4	12	3	15
5	7½	10¼	4½	13½	3½	17
6	8	11½	5	14½	3½	18
8	9	14	5½	17½	4½	22
10	11	16½	6½	20½	5	25½
12	12	19	7½	24½	5½	30
14	14	21½	7½			
16	15	24	8			
18	16½	26½	8½			
20	18	29	9½			
24	22	34	11			

250 Pound Cast Iron Flanged Fittings

Size	Dimensions in Inches					
	A	B	C	D	E	F
2	5		3	9	2½	11½
2½	5½		3½	10½	2½	13
3	6		3½	11	3	14
3½	6½		4			
4	7		4½	13½	3	16½
5	8		5	15	3½	18½
6	8½		5½	17½	4	21½
8	10		6	20½	5	25½
10	11½		7	24	5½	29½
12	13		8	27½	6	33½

Note: 250 pound flanges have a $\frac{1}{16}$ inch raised face.

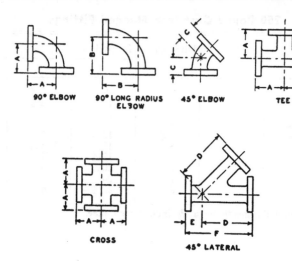

Cast iron flanged fittings.

STANDARD COMPANION FLANGES AND BOLTS

(For working pressure up to 125 pounds)

Size, in Inches	Diameter of Flange, in Inches	Bolt Circle, in Inches	No. of Bolts	Size of Bolts, in Inches	Length of Bolts, in Inches
¾	3½	2½	4	⅜	1½
1	4¼	3⅛	4	½	1¾
1¼	4⅝	3½	4	½	2
1½	5	3⅞	4	½	2
2	6	4¾	4	⅝	2¼
2½	7	5½	4	⅝	2½
3	7½	6	4	⅝	2½
3½	8½	7	8	⅝	2¾
4	9	7½	8	⅝	3
5	10	8½	8	¾	3
6	11	9½	8	¾	3¼
8	13½	11¾	8	¾	3½
10	16	14¼	12	⅞	3¾
12	19	17	12	⅞	3¾
14	21	18¾	12	1	4¼
16	23½	21¼	16	1	4½

EXTRA HEAVY COMPANION FLANGES AND BOLTS

Pipe Sizes Inches	Dia. of Flanges	Dia. of Bolt Circle	No. of Bolts	Dia. of Bolts	Lgth. of Bolts
1	4⅞	3½	4	⅝	2½
1¼	5¼	3⅞	4	⅝	2½
1½	6⅛	4½	4	¾	2¾
2	6½	5	8	⅝	2¾
2½	7½	5⅞	8	¾	3¼
3	8¼	6⅝	8	¾	3½
3½	9	7¼	8	¾	3½
4	10	7⅞	8	¾	3¾
5	11	9¼	8	¾	4
6	12½	10⅝	12	¾	4
8	15	13	12	⅞	4½
10	17½	15¼	16	1	5¼
12	20½	17¾	16	1⅛	5½
14 O.D.	23	20¼	20	1⅛	6
16 O.D.	25½	22½	20	1¼	6¼
18 O.D.	28	24¾	24	1¼	6½
20 O.D.	30½	27	24	1¼	6¾
24 O.D.	36	32	24	1½	7¾
30 O.D.	43	39¼	28	1¾	8½
36 O.D.	50	46	32	2	9½
42 O.D.	57	52¾	36	2	10¼
48 O.D.	65	60¾	40	2	10¾

DRILL SIZES FOR PIPE TAPS

Size of Tap in Inches	Number of Threads per Inch	Diameter of Drill	Size of Tap in Inches	Number of Threads per Inch	Diameter of Drill
1/8	27	11/32	2	11½	2 3/16
1/4	18	7/16	2½	8	2 9/16
3/8	18	37/64	3	8	3 3/16
1/2	14	23/32	3½	8	3 11/16
3/4	14	59/64	4	8	4 3/16
1	11½	1 5/32	4½	8	4 3/4
1¼	11½	1½	5	8	5 3/16
1½	11½	1 47/64	6	8	6 3/16

TAP AND DRILL SIZES
(American Standard Coarse)

Size of Drill	Size of Tap	Threads per Inch	Size of Drill	Size of Tap	Threads per Inch
7	1/4	20	49/64	7/8	9
F	5/16	18	49/64	15/16	9
5/16	3/8	16	7/8	1	8
U	7/16	14	1 7/64	1 1/8	7
27/64	1/2	13	1 7/32	1 1/4	7
31/64	9/16	12	1 17/64	1 3/8	6
17/32	5/8	11	1 11/32	1 1/2	6
19/32	11/16	11	1 29/64	1 5/8	5½
21/32	3/4	10	1 9/16	1 3/4	5
23/32	13/16	10	1 11/16	1 7/8	5
			1 25/32	2	4½

STANDARD PIPE DATA

Nominal Pipe Diameter, in Inches	Inside Diameter, in Inches	Outside Diameter, in Inches	Outside Circumference, in Inches	Inside Area, in Square Inches	Weight per Lineal Foot	Wall Thickness, in Inches
⅛	.269	.405	1.272	.057	.244	.068
¼	.364	.540	1.696	.104	.424	.088
⅜	.493	.675	2.121	.191	.567	.091
½	.622	.840	2.639	.304	.850	.109
¾	.824	1.050	3.299	.533	1.130	.113
1	1.049	1.315	4.131	.864	1.678	.133
1¼	1.380	1.660	5.215	1.496	2.272	.140
1½	1.610	1.900	5.969	2.036	2.717	.145
2	2.067	2.375	7.461	3.356	3.652	.154
2½	2.469	2.875	9.032	4.788	5.793	.203
3	3.068	3.500	10.996	7.393	7.575	.216
3½	3.548	4.000	12.566	9.887	9.109	.226
4	4.026	4.500	14.137	12.730	10.790	.237
5	5.047	5.563	17.475	20.006	14.617	.258
6	6.065	6.625	20.813	28.890	18.974	.280

STANDARD PIPE DATA (Cont'd)

Nominal Pipe Diameter, in Inches	Inside Diameter, in Inches	Outside Diameter, in Inches	Outside Circumference, in Inches	Inside Area, in Square Inches	Weight per Lineal Foot	Wall Thickness, in Inches
8	7.981	8.625	27.096	50.027	28.544	.322
10	10.020	10.750	33.772	78.854	40.483	.365
12	12.000	12.750	40.055	113.098	48.995	.375
14	13.250	14.000	43.982	137.886	53.941	.375
16	15.250	16.000	50.265	182.650	61.746	.375
18	17.250	18.000	56.549	233.710	69.753	.375
20	19.250	20.000	62.832	291.039	77.619	.375
24	23.250	24.000	75.398	424.560	93.509	.375
26	25.250	26.000	81.682	500.742	101.435	.375
30	29.250	30.000	94.248	671.959	117.267	.375
36	35.250	36.000	113.097	975.909	141.017	.375
42	41.250	42.000	131.947	1336.404	164.640	.375

COPPER TUBE — Type K*

Nominal Pipe Size, in Inches	Outside Diameter, in Inches	Inside Diameter, in Inches	Wall Thickness, in Inches	Inside Area, in Square Inches	Weight per Lineal Foot, in Pounds
¼	.375	.305	.035	.073	.145
⅜	.500	.402	.049	.127	.269
½	.625	.527	.049	.218	.344
⅝	.750	.652	.049	.334	.418
¾	.875	.745	.065	.436	.641
1	1.125	.995	.065	.778	.839
1¼	1.375	1.245	.065	1.220	1.040
1½	1.625	1.481	.072	1.720	1.360
2	2.125	1.959	.083	3.010	2.060
2½	2.625	2.435	.095	4.666	2.932
3	3.125	2.907	.109	6.655	4.000
3½	3.625	3.385	.120	9.000	5.122
4	4.125	3.857	.134	11.683	6.511
5	5.125	4.805	.160	18.132	9.672
6	6.125	5.741	.192	25.883	13.912
8	8.125	7.583	.271	45.160	25.900
10	10.125	9.449	.338	70.122	40.322
12	12.125	11.315	.405	100.555	57.802

*Use for underground gas, oil, and water lines and for plumbing and heating systems above ground. Has thick wall. Furnished in hard and soft copper. Can be bent cold. Weight: .323 lbs. per cu. in.

COPPER TUBE — Type L*

Nominal Pipe Size, in Inches	Outside Diameter, in Inches	Inside Diameter, in Inches	Wall Thickness, in Inches	Inside Area, in Square Inches	Weight per Lineal Foot, in Pounds
1/4	.375	.315	.030	.078	.126
3/8	.500	.430	.035	.145	.198
1/2	.625	.545	.040	.233	.285
5/8	.750	.666	.042	.348	.362
3/4	.875	.785	.045	.484	.455
1	1.125	1.025	.050	.825	.655
1 1/4	1.375	1.265	.055	1.260	.884
1 1/2	1.625	1.505	.060	1.780	1.111
2	2.125	1.985	.070	3.090	1.750
2 1/2	2.625	2.465	.080	4.770	2.480
3	3.125	2.945	.090	6.811	3.333
3 1/2	3.625	3.425	.100	9.211	4.290
4	4.125	3.905	.110	11.950	5.382
5	5.125	4.875	.125	18.666	7.611
6	6.125	5.845	.140	26.800	10.201
8	8.125	7.725	.200	46.860	19.301
10	10.125	9.625	.250	72.760	30.060
12	12.125	11.565	.280	105.000	40.390

*Use for plumbing and heating systems. Medium wall thickness. Furnished in hard and soft copper. Can be bent cold. Weight: 323 lbs. per cu. in.

COPPER TUBE — Type M*

Nominal Pipe Size, in Inches	Outside Diameter, in Inches	Inside Diameter, in Inches	Wall Thickness, in Inches	Inside Area, in Square Inches	Weight per Lineal Foot, in Pounds
1/4	.375	.325	.025	.083	.107
3/8	.500	.450	.025	.159	.145
1/2	.625	.569	.028	.254	.204
5/8	.750	.690	.030	.374	.263
3/4	.875	.811	.032	.517	.328
1	1.125	1.055	.035	.874	.465
1¼	1.375	1.291	.042	1.310	.682
1½	1.625	1.527	.049	1.830	.940
2	2.125	2.009	.058	2.170	1.460
2½	2.625	2.495	.065	4.890	2.030
3	3.125	2.981	.072	6.980	2.680
3½	3.625	3.459	.083	9.400	3.580
4	4.125	3.935	.095	12.200	4.660
5	5.125	4.907	.109	18.900	6.660
6	6.125	5.881	.122	27.200	8.920
8	8.125	7.785	.170	47.590	16.480
10	10.125	9.701	.212	73.900	25.590
12	12.125	11.617	.254	106.000	36.710

*Use for waste interior drainage, vents, and other non-pressure applications. Bending not recommended. Use with solder fittings only. Thin wall thickness. Furnished in hard temper only. Weight: .323 lbs. per cu. in.

POLYVINYL CHLORIDE PLASTIC PIPE (PVC)
Normal-Impact*

	Nominal Pipe Size, in Inches	Outside Diameter, in Inches	Inside Diameter, in Inches	Wall Thickness, in Inches	Approx. Weight per Foot, in Pounds	Maximum Operating Pressure at Maximum Temperature of 150°	
						Plain End	Threaded
Schedule A	½	.840	.750	.045	.070	80	Threading Not Recommended
	¾	1.050	.940	.055	.104	80	
	1	1.315	1.195	.060	.142	70	
	1¼	1.660	1.520	.070	.211	65	
	1½	1.900	1.740	.080	.275	65	
	2	2.375	2.175	.100	.428	65	
	2½	2.875	2.635	.120	.620	65	
	3	3.500	3.220	.140	.885	65	
	4	4.500	4.110	.195	1.580	65	

*Maximum operating temperature is 150° F.

Standard lengths are 10 and 20 feet with plain ends.

Manufacturer will furnish special cut lengths.

Joints are made by threading, solvent cementing, or heat welding.

Pipe can be bent. Bending must be done hot. Use a uniform heat of 250° to 275° F. Avoid overheating. Avoid flattening by filling pipe with dry sand or using a coil spring in the bending zone. Cool with compressed air or cold water.

POLYVINYL CHLORIDE PLASTIC PIPE (PVC)
Normal-Impact (Cont'd)

	Nominal Pipe Size, in Inches	Outside Diameter, in Inches	Inside Diameter, in Inches	Wall Thickness, in Inches	Approx. Weight per Foot, in Pounds	Maximum Operating Pressure at Maximum Temperature of 150°	
						Plain End	Threaded
Schedule 40	½	.840	.622	.109	.152	220	Threading Not Recommended
	¾	1.050	.824	.113	.203	180	
	1	1.315	1.049	.133	.300	170	
	1¼	1.660	1.380	.140	.405	140	
	1½	1.900	1.610	.145	.485	125	
	2	2.375	2.067	.154	.653	115	
	2½	2.875	2.469	.203	1.035	110	
	3	3.500	3.068	.216	1.352	100	
	4	4.500	4.026	.237	1.920	85	
	6	6.625	6.065	.280	3.445	65	
Schedule 80	½	.840	.546	.147	.195	310	175
	¾	1.050	.742	.154	.263	255	150
	1	1.315	.957	.179	.389	240	145
	1¼	1.660	1.278	.191	.535	195	120

POLYVINYL CHLORIDE PLASTIC PIPE (PVC)
Normal-Impact (Cont'd)

	Nominal Pipe Size, in Inches	Outside Diameter, in Inches	Inside Diameter, in Inches	Wall Thickness, in Inches	Approx. Weight per Foot, in Pounds	Maximum Operating Pressure at Maximum Temperature of 150°	
						Plain End	Threaded
Schedule 80 (Cont'd)	1½	1.900	1.500	.200	.649	175	110
	2	2.375	1.939	.218	.892	150	100
	2½	2.875	2.323	.276	1.385	140	100
	3	3.500	2.900	.300	1.852	140	95
	4	4.500	3.826	.337	2.701	120	85
	6	6.625	5.761	.432	5.152	110	80
Schedule 120	½	.840	.500	.170	.218	360	220
	¾	1.050	.710	.170	.285	270	170
	1	1.315	.915	.200	.425	255	160
	1¼	1.660	1.230	.215	.593	215	140
	1½	1.900	1.450	.225	.721	190	130
	2	2.375	1.875	.250	1.020	170	120
	2½	2.875	2.275	.300	1.500	170	110
	3	3.500	2.800	.350	2.130	160	110
	4	4.500	3.624	.438	3.382	155	110
	6	6.625	5.501	.562	6.503	145	110

POLYVINYL CHLORIDE PLASTIC PIPE (PVC)
High-Impact*

	Nominal Pipe Size, in Inches	Outside Diameter, in Inches	Inside Diameter, in Inches	Wall Thickness, in Inches	Approx. Weight per Foot, Pounds	Maximum Operating Pressure at Maximum Temperature of 130°	
						Plain End	Threaded
Schedule A	½	.840	.750	.045	.068	35	Threading Not Recommended
	¾	1.050	.940	.055	.101	35	
	1	1.315	1.195	.060	.138	30	
	1¼	1.660	1.520	.070	.205	25	
	1½	1.900	1.740	.080	.268	25	
	2	2.375	2.175	.100	.412	25	
	2½	2.875	2.635	.120	.608	25	
	3	3.500	3.220	.140	.865	25	
	4	4.500	4.110	.195	1.545	25	

*Maximum operating temperature is 130° F.
Standard lengths are 10 and 20 feet with plain ends.
Manufacturer will furnish special cut lengths.
Joints are made by threading, solvent cementing, or heat welding.

Pipe can be bent. Bending must be done hot. Use a uniform heat of 250° to 275° F. Avoid overheating. Avoid flattening by filling pipe with dry sand or using a coil spring in the bending zone. Cool with compressed air or cold water.

POLYVINYL CHLORIDE PLASTIC PIPE (PVC)
High-Impact (Cont'd)

	Nominal Pipe Size, in Inches	Outside Diameter, in Inches	Inside Diameter, in Inches	Wall Thickness, in Inches	Approx. Weight per Foot, Pounds	Maximum Operating Pressure at Maximum Temperature of 130°	
						Plain End	Threaded
Schedule 40	½	.840	.622	.109	.146	90	Threading Not Recommended
	¾	1.050	.824	.113	.195	70	
	1	1.315	1.049	.133	.289	70	
	1¼	1.660	1.380	.140	.391	50	
	1½	1.900	1.610	.145	.467	45	
	2	2.375	2.067	.154	.629	45	
	2½	2.875	2.469	.203	.997	45	
	3	3.500	3.068	.216	1.303	40	
	4	4.500	4.026	.237	1.857	30	
	6	6.625	6.065	.280	3.266	30	
Schedule 80	½	.840	.546	.147	.187	120	70
	¾	1.050	.742	.154	.195	100	60
	1	1.315	.957	.179	.289	95	55
	1¼	1.660	1.278	.191	.391	80	50

POLYVINYL CHLORIDE PLASTIC PIPE (PVC)
High-Impact (Cont'd)

	Nominal Pipe Size, in Inches	Outside Diameter, in Inches	Inside Diameter, in Inches	Wall Thickness, in Inches	Approx. Weight per Foot, Pounds	Maximum Operating Pressure at Maximum Temperature of 130°	
						Plain End	Threaded
Schedule 80 (Cont'd)	1½	1.900	1.500	.200	.467	70	45
	2	2.375	1.939	.218	.629	60	40
	2½	2.875	2.323	.276	.998	60	40
	3	3.500	2.900	.300	1.303	55	35
	4	4.500	3.826	.337	1.855	50	35
	6	6.625	5.761	.432	3.265	40	30
Schedule 120	½	.840	.500	.170	.208	145	90
	¾	1.050	.710	.170	.273	110	70
	1	1.315	.915	.200	.410	105	65
	1¼	1.660	1.230	.215	.571	85	55
	1½	1.900	1.450	.225	.691	80	55
	2	2.375	1.875	.250	.975	70	50
	2½	2.875	2.275	.300	1.419	70	45
	3	3.500	2.800	.350	2.027	65	45
	4	4.500	3.624	.438	3.280	65	45
	6	6.625	5.501	.562	6.265	55	45

SUPPORT SPACING FOR POLYVINYL CHLORIDE PLASTIC PIPE (PVC)

	Pipe Size, in Inches	Support Spacing in Feet — Temperature in Deg. F.					
		60°	80°	100°	120°	130°	140°
Schedule 40	1/2	5.50	5.20	4.83	4.20	3.75	3.20
	3/4	5.50	5.20	4.83	4.20	3.75	3.20
	1	6.16	5.75	5.41	4.50	4.00	3.50
	1 1/4	6.16	5.75	5.41	4.50	4.00	3.50
	1 1/2	6.50	6.16	5.75	4.83	4.33	3.75
	2	6.50	6.16	5.75	4.83	4.33	3.75
	2 1/2	7.75	7.20	6.83	5.83	5.16	4.50
	3	7.75	7.20	6.83	5.83	5.16	4.50
	4	8.00	7.50	7.16	6.00	5.41	4.75
	6	8.75	8.20	7.75	6.41	5.83	5.00
Schedule 80	1/2	6.50	6.00	5.75	4.83	4.33	3.75
	3/4	6.50	6.00	5.75	4.83	4.33	3.75
	1	7.00	6.66	6.20	5.20	4.66	4.00
	1 1/4	7.33	6.91	6.41	5.50	4.83	4.20
	1 1/2	7.33	6.91	6.41	5.50	4.83	4.20
	2	7.75	7.20	6.83	5.83	5.16	4.50

SUPPORT SPACING FOR POLYVINYL CHLORIDE PLASTIC PIPE (PVC) (Cont'd)

	Pipe Size, in Inches	Support Spacing in Feet — Temperature in Deg. F.					
		60°	80°	100°	120°	130°	140°
Schedule 80 (Cont'd)	2½	9.00	8.50	8.00	6.83	6.00	5.20
	3	9.00	8.50	8.00	6.83	6.00	5.20
	4	9.66	8.91	8.41	7.16	6.41	5.66
	6	10.83	10.16	9.50	8.00	7.20	6.33
Schedule 120	½	6.83	6.41	6.00	5.00	4.50	3.91
	¾	6.83	6.41	6.00	5.00	4.50	3.91
	1	7.41	7.00	6.50	5.50	4.91	4.20
	1¼	7.75	7.20	6.83	5.83	5.16	4.50
	1½	7.75	7.20	6.83	5.83	5.16	4.50
	2	8.20	7.75	7.20	6.16	5.50	4.83
	2½	9.83	9.20	8.66	7.20	6.50	5.66
	3	9.83	9.20	8.66	7.20	6.50	5.66
	4	11.00	10.20	9.66	8.16	7.33	6.33
	6	12.33	11.50	10.91	9.20	8.20	7.16

BENDING RADIUS FOR POLYVINYL CHLORIDE PLASTIC PIPE (PVC)

Pipe Size, in Inches	Minimum Bending Radius		Pipe Size, in Inches	Minimum Bending Radius
1/2	2 1/4		2	10
3/4	3 1/2		2 1/2	12 1/2
1	4 1/2		3	15
1 1/4	6 1/4		4	20
1 1/2	7		6	35

UNITED STATES STANDARD GAUGE FOR SHEET STEEL

Number of Gauge	Approximate Thickness, in Fractions of an Inch	Approximate Thickness, in Decimal Parts of an Inch	Weight per Square Foot, in Pounds
11	1/8	.125	5.0
12	7/64	.109	4.375
13	3/32	.094	3.75
14	5/64	.078	3.125
16	1/16	.062	2.5
18	1/20	.05	2.0
20	3/80	.0375	1.5
22	1/32	.03125	1.25
24	1/40	.025	1.00
26	3/160	.01875	0.75
28	1/64	.0156	0.625
30	1/80	.0125	0.5

Note: To find the weight of sheet steel, multiply the thickness in decimals by 40.8. The result will be the weight in pounds per square foot.

Example: If a piece of sheet steel is .005 in. thick, its weight is .005 times 40.8, which equals .204 pound per square foot.

USEFUL INFORMATION ON VARIOUS MATERIALS

Material	Chemical Symbol	Weight, in Pounds per Cubic Inch	Weight, in Pounds per Cubic Foot	Melting Point, Degrees Fahrenheit
Aluminum	Al	.093	160	1218
Antimony	Sb	.2422	418	1150
Brass	..	.303	524	1800
Bronze	..	.320	552	1700
Chromium	Cr	.2348	406	2740
Copper	Cu	.323	558	2450
Gold	Au	.6975	1205	1975
Iron (cast)	Fe	.260	450	2450
Iron (wrought)	Fe	.2834	490	2900
Lead	Pb	.4105	710	620
Manganese	Mn	.2679	463	2200
Mercury	Hg	.491	849	39.5
Molybdenum	Mo	.309	534	4500
Monel	..	.318	550	2480
Platinum	Pt	.818	1413	3200
Steel (mild)	Fe	.2816	490	2600
Steel (stainless)	..	.277	484	2750
Tin	Sn	.265	459	450
Titanium	Ti	.1278	221	3360
Zinc	Zn	.258	446	787

BOILING POINTS OF WATER AT VARIOUS PRESSURES

Vacuum, in Inches of Mercury	Boiling Point	Vacuum, in Inches of Mercury	Boiling Point
29	76.62	7	198.87
28	99.93	6	200.96
27	114.22	5	202.25
26	124.77	4	204.85
25	133.22	3	206.70
24	140.31	2	208.50
23	146.45	1	210.25
22	151.87	Gauge Lbs.	
21	156.75	0	212.
20	161.19	1	215.6
19	165.24	2	218.5
18	169.00	4	224.4
17	172.51	6	229.8
16	175.80	8	234.8
15	178.91	10	239.4
14	181.82	15	249.8
13	184.61	25	266.8
12	187.21	50	297.7
11	189.75	75	320.1
10	192.19	100	337.9
9	194.50	125	352.9
8	196.73	200	387.9

WATER PRESSURE IN POUNDS WITH EQUIVALENT HEADS

Pounds per Square Inch	Feet Head	Pounds per Square Inch	Feet Head
1	2.31	100	230.90
2	4.62	110	253.98
3	6.93	120	277.07
4	9.24	130	300.16
5	11.54	140	323.25
6	13.85	150	346.34
7	16.16	160	369.43
8	18.47	170	392.52
9	20.78	180	415.61
10	23.09	200	461.78
15	34.63	250	577.24
20	46.18	300	692.69
25	57.72	350	808.13
30	69.27	400	922.58
40	92.36	500	1154.48
50	115.45	600	1385.39
60	138.54	700	1616.30
70	161.63	800	1847.20
80	184.72	900	2078.10
90	207.81	1000	2309.00

Note: One pound of pressure per square inch of water equals 2.309 feet of water at 62° Fahrenheit. Therefore, to find the feet head of water for any pressure not given in the table above, multiply the pressure pounds per square inch by 2.309.

HEADS OF WATER IN FEET WITH EQUIVALENT PRESSURES

Feet Head	Pounds per Square Inch	Feet Head	Pounds per Square Inch
1	.43	100	43.31
2	.87	110	47.64
3	1.30	120	51.97
4	1.73	130	56.30
5	2.17	140	60.63
6	2.60	150	64.96
7	3.03	160	69.29
8	3.46	170	73.63
9	3.90	180	77.96
10	4.33	200	86.62
15	6.50	250	108.27
20	8.66	300	129.93
25	10.83	350	151.58
30	12.99	400	173.24
40	17.32	500	216.55
50	21.65	600	259.85
60	25.99	700	303.16
70	30.32	800	346.47
80	34.65	900	389.78
90	38.98	1000	433.00

Note: One foot of water at 62° Fahrenheit equals .433 pound pressure per square inch. To find the pressure per square inch for any feet head not given in the table above, multiply the feet head by .433.

USEFUL INFORMATION

Boilers

● To ascertain the heating surface in tubular boilers, multiply ⅔ of the circumference of the boiler by the length of the boiler in inches and add to it the area of all the tubes.

● Each square foot of heating surface is considered sufficient to evaporate 2 pounds of water. Therefore, for one engine using 30 pounds of water per horse power per hour, each horse power of the engine requires 15 square feet of heating surface in the boiler.

● Well-designed boilers, under successful operation, will evaporate from 7 to 10 pounds of water per pound of first class coal.

● One-sixth of the tensile strength of plate, multiplied by the thickness of the plate and divided by ½ the diameter of the boiler gives the safe working pressure for tubular boilers. For marine boilers, add 20 per cent for drilled holes.

● Double riveting is from 16 to 20 per cent stronger than single riveting.

Fuel

● One cubic foot of anthracite coal weighs about 53 pounds.

● One cubic foot of bituminous coal weighs 47 to 50 pounds.

● A ton of coal is equivalent to two cords of wood for steam purposes.

● Two and one-quarter pounds of dry wood is equal to 1 pound of average-quality soft coal.

● An average of 10 to 12 pounds of hard coal or 18 to 20 pounds of soft coal can be burned per hour with natural draft on 1 square foot of fire grate.

● A saving of about 1 per cent in fuel can be effected for every 11° that the fuel water is warmed. With exhaust steam available, if cold water at 70° is raised to 212° Fahrenheit, the saving of fuel will approximate 12 per cent.

Piping

● The area of a pipe wall may be determined by the following formula:
Area of pipe wall = .7854 x [(O.D. x O.D.) — (I.D. x I.D.)]

● The capacity of pipes is as the square of their diameters. Thus, doubling the diameter of a pipe increases its capacity four times.

● The approximate weight of a piece of pipe may be determined by the following formulas:

Cast Iron Pipe: weight = $(A^2 - B^2)$ x L x .2042

Steel Pipe: weight = $(A^2 - B^2)$ x L x .2199

Copper Pipe: weight = $(A^2 - B^2)$ x L x .2537

A = outside diameter of the pipe in inches

B = inside diameter of the pipe in inches

L = length of the pipe in inches

Example:

Determine the weight of a piece of 4 inch steel pipe 12 ft. long.
A = 4.5 in.
B = 4 in.

L = 12 x 12 = 144 in.
Weight = $(4.5^2 - 4^2)$ x 144 x .2199 = 134.578 pounds

Radiation

● Three feet of 1-in. pipe equal 1 square foot of radiation.

● Two and one-third lineal feet of 1¼-in. pipe equal 1 square foot of radiation.

● Hot water radiation gives off 150 B.T.U. per square foot of radiation per hour.

● Steam radiation gives off 240 B.T.U. per square foot of radiation per hour.

● On greenhouse heating, figure ⅔ square foot of radiation per square foot of glass.

● One square foot of direct radiation condenses .25 pound of water per hour.

Formulas for Pipe Radiation:

$$L = \frac{144}{D \times 3.1416} \times R \div 12$$

D = O.D. of pipe
L = length of pipe needed in ft.
R = sq. ft. of radiation needed

Example:

How many feet of 2-in. pipe are required to furnish 30 sq. ft. of radiation?

D = 2.375 in.
R = 30 sq. ft.

$$L = \frac{144}{2.375 \times 3.1416} \times 30 \div 12 = 48'3''$$

Steam

● Designers of steam piping figure on a steam travel of about 1½ miles per minute. Very often it is much more.

● Steam rising from water at its boiling point at 212° has a pressure equal to the atmosphere (14.7 pounds per square inch).

Water

● A cubic foot of water contains 7½ gallons, 1728 cubic inches, and weighs 62½ pounds.

● A gallon of water weighs 8⅓ pounds and contains 231 cubic inches.

● Water expands 1/23 of its volume when heated from 40° to 212°.

● The height of a column of water, equal to a pressure of 1 pound per square inch, is 2.31 feet.

● To find the pressure in pounds per square inch of a column of water, multiply the height of the column in feet by .434.

● The average pressure of the atmosphere is estimated at 14.7 pounds per square inch so that with a perfect vacuum it will sustain a column of water 34 feet high.

● The friction of water in pipes varies as the square of the velocity.

● To evaporate 1 cubic foot of water requires the consumption of 7½ pounds of ordinary coal or about 1 pound of coal to 1 gallon of water.

● A cubic inch of water evaporated at atmospheric pressure is converted into approximately 1 cubic foot of steam.

Temperature

● Degrees C. = deg. F. — 32 ÷ 1.8
● Degrees F. = deg. C. x 1.8 + 32

● To figure the final temperature when two different temperatures of water are mixed together, use the following formula:

$$\text{Final temperature} = \frac{(A \times C) + (B \times D)}{A + B}$$

A = weight of lower temperature water

B = weight of higher temperature water

C = lower temperature

D = higher temperature

Example:

What will be the final temperature of the water if 30 pounds of water at 140° Fahrenheit is mixed with 70 pounds of water at 210° Fahrenheit, not counting radiation loss and absorbtion of heat by the container.

A = 30 pounds
B = 70 pounds
C = 140° Fahrenheit
D = 210° Fahrenheit

$$\text{Final temperature} = \frac{(30 \times 140) + (70 \times 210)}{30 + 70} = 189°$$
Fahrenheit

FORMULAS

Circle

Circumference = diameter × 3.1416

Circumference = radius × 6.2832

Diameter = radius × 2

Diameter = square root of;
(area ÷ .7854)

Diameter = square root of area
× 1.1283

Diameter = circumference × .31831

Radius = diameter ÷ 2

Radius = circumference × .15915

Radius = square root of area × .56419

Area = diameter × diameter × .7854

Area = half of the circumference ×
half of the diameter

Area = square of the circumference
× .0796

Arc length = degrees × radius × .01745

Degrees of arc = length ÷ (radius ×
.01745)

Radius of arc = length ÷ (degrees ×
.01745)

Side of equal square = diameter × .8862

Side of inscribed square = diameter ×
.7071

Area of sector = area of circle × degrees of arc ÷ 360

Cone

Area of surface = one-half of circumference of base ×
slant height + area
of base.

Volume = diameter × diameter × .7854
× one-third of the altitude.

Cube

Volume = width × height × length.

Cylinder

Area of surface = diameter × 3.1416 × length + area of the two bases

Area of base = diameter × diameter × .7854

Area of base = volume ÷ length

Length = volume ÷ area of base

Volume = length × area of base

Capacity in gallons = volume in inches ÷ 231

Capacity in gallons = diameter × diameter × length × .0034

Capacity in gallons = volume in feet × 7.48

Ellipse

Area = short diameter × long diameter × .7854.

Hexagon

Area = width of side × 2.598 × width of side.

Parallelogram

Area = base × distance between the two parallel sides.

Pyramid

Area = ½ perimeter of base × slant height + area of base.

Volume = area of base × ⅓ of the altitude.

Rectangle

Area = length × width.

Rectangular Prism

Volume = width × height × length.

Sphere

Area of surface = diameter × diameter
× 3.1416.

Side of inscribed cube = radius ×
1.1547.

Volume = diameter × diameter × diameter × .5236.

Square

Area = length × width.

Triangle

Area = one-half of height times base.

Trapezoid

Area = one-half of the sum of the parallel sides × the height.

WEIGHTS AND MEASURES

Linear Measure

12 inches	= 1 foot
3 feet	= 1 yard
5½ yards	= 1 rod
320 rods	= 1 mile
1 mile	= 1760 yards
1 mile	= 5280 feet

Square Measure

144 square inches	= 1 square foot
9 square feet	= 1 square yard
1 square yard	= 1296 square inches
4840 square yards	= 1 acre
640 acres	= 1 square mile

Cubic Measure

1728 cubic inches	= 1 cubic foot
27 cubic feet	= 1 cubic yard

Avoirdupois Weight

16 ounces	= 1 pound
100 pounds	= 1 hundredweight
20 hundredweight	= 1 ton
1 ton	= 2000 pounds
1 long ton	= 2240 pounds

Liquid Measure

4 gills	= 1 pint
2 pints	= 1 quart
4 quarts	= 1 gallon
31½ gallons	= 1 barrel
1 gallon	= 231 cubic inches
7.48 gallons	= 1 cubic foot
1 gallon water	= 8.33 pounds
1 gallon gasoline	= 5.84 pounds

MULTIPLIERS THAT ARE USEFUL TO THE TRADE

To Change	To	Multiply by
Inches	Feet	0.0833
Inches	Millimeters	25.4
Feet	Inches	12
Feet	Yards	0.3333
Yards	Feet	3
Square inches	Square feet	0.00694
Square feet	Square inches	144
Square feet	Square yards	0.11111
Square yards	Square feet	9
Cubic inches	Cubic feet	0.00058
Cubic feet	Cubic inches	1728
Cubic feet	Cubic yards	0.03703
Cubic yards	Cubic feet	27
Cubic inches	Gallons	0.00433
Cubic feet	Gallons	7.48
Gallons	Cubic inches	231
Gallons	Cubic feet	0.1337
Gallons	Pounds of water	8.33
Pounds of water	Gallons	0.12004
Ounces	Pounds	0.0625
Pounds	Ounces	16

MULTIPLIERS THAT ARE USEFUL TO THE TRADE (Cont'd)

To Change	To	Multiply by
Inches of water...............	Pounds per square inch............	0.0361
Inches of water...............	Inches of mercury.................	0.0735
Inches of water...............	Ounces per square inch..........	0.578
Inches of water...............	Pounds per square foot...........	5.2
Inches of mercury............	Inches of water	13.6
Inches of mercury............	Feet of water....................	1.1333
Inches of mercury............	Pounds per square inch..........	0.4914
Ounces per square inch........	Inches of mercury.............	0.127
Ounces per square inch........	Inches of water	1.733
Pounds per square inch........	Inches of water	27.72
Pounds per square inch........	Feet of water....................	2.310
Pounds per square inch........	Inches of mercury.............	2.04
Pounds per square inch........	Atmospheres	0.0681
Feet of water.................	Pounds per square inch.........	0.434
Feet of water.................	Pounds per square foot...........	62.5
Feet of water.................	Inches of mercury...............	0.8824
Atmospheres	Pounds per square inch.........	14.696
Atmospheres	Inches of mercury...............	29.92
Atmospheres	Feet of water	34
Long tons	Pounds	2240
Short tons	Pounds	2000
Short tons	Long tons	0.89285

DECIMAL EQUIVALENTS OF FRACTIONS OF AN INCH

Inches	Decimal of an Inch	Inches	Decimal of an Inch
1/64	.015625	33/64	.515625
1/32	.03125	17/32	.53125
3/64	.046875	35/64	.546875
1/16	.0625	9/16	.5625
5/64	.078125	37/64	.578125
3/32	.09375	19/32	.59375
7/64	.109375	39/64	.609375
1/8	.125	5/8	.625
9/64	.140625	41/64	.640625
5/32	.15625	21/32	.65625
11/64	.171875	43/64	.671875
3/16	.1875	11/16	.6875
13/64	.203125	45/64	.703125
7/32	.21875	23/32	.71875
15/64	.234375	47/64	.734375
1/4	.25	3/4	.75
17/64	.265625	49/64	.765625
9/32	.28125	25/32	.78125
19/64	.296875	51/64	.796875
5/16	.3125	13/16	.8125
21/64	.328125	53/64	.828125
11/32	.34375	27/32	.84375
23/64	.359375	55/64	.859375
3/8	.375	7/8	.875
25/64	.390625	57/64	.890625
13/32	.40625	29/32	.90625
27/64	.421875	59/64	.921875
7/16	.4375	15/16	.9375
29/64	.453125	61/64	.953125
15/32	.46875	31/32	.96875
31/64	.484375	63/64	.984375
1/2	.5	1	1.

See note on bottom of page 179.

MINUTES CONVERTED TO DECIMALS OF A DEGREE

Min.	Deg.	Min.	Deg.	Min.	Deg.	Min.	Deg.	Min.	Deg.	Min.	Deg.
1	.0166	11	.1833	21	.3500	31	.5166	41	.6833	51	.8500
2	.0333	12	.2000	22	.3666	32	.5333	42	.7000	52	.8666
3	.0500	13	.2166	23	.3833	33	.5500	43	.7166	53	.8833
4	.0666	14	.2333	24	.4000	34	.5666	44	.7333	54	.9000
5	.0833	15	.2500	25	.4166	35	.5833	45	.7500	55	.9166
6	.1000	16	.2666	26	.4333	36	.6000	46	.7666	56	.9333
7	.1166	17	.2833	27	.4500	37	.6166	47	.7833	57	.9500
8	.1333	18	.3000	28	.4666	38	.6333	48	.8000	58	.9666
9	.1500	19	.3166	29	.4833	39	.6500	49	.8166	59	.9833
10	.1666	20	.3333	30	.5000	40	.6666	50	.8333	60	1.0000

Note: Referring to page 178, to find the decimal equivalent of a fraction, divide the numerator by the denominator.

Example: Reduce the fraction ¾ to a decimal.

$$
\begin{array}{r}
.75 \\
4\overline{)3.00} \\
28 \\
\hline
20 \\
20 \\
\hline
\end{array}
$$

INCHES CONVERTED TO DECIMALS OF FEET

Inches	Decimal of a Foot	Inches	Decimal of a Foot	Inches	Decimal of a Foot
1/8	.01042	3 1/8	.26042	6 1/4	.52083
1/4	.02083	3 1/4	.27083	6 1/2	.54167
3/8	.03125	3 3/8	.28125	6 3/4	.56250
1/2	.04167	3 1/2	.29167	7	.58333
5/8	.05208	3 5/8	.30208	7 1/4	.60417
3/4	.06250	3 3/4	.31250	7 1/2	.62500
7/8	.07291	3 7/8	.32292	7 3/4	.64583
1	.08333	4	.33333	8	.66666
1 1/8	.09375	4 1/8	.34375	8 1/4	.68750
1 1/4	.10417	4 1/4	.35417	8 1/2	.70833
1 3/8	.11458	4 3/8	.36458	8 3/4	.72917
1 1/2	.12500	4 1/2	.37500	9	.75000
1 5/8	.13542	4 5/8	.38542	9 1/4	.77083
1 3/4	.14583	4 3/4	.39583	9 1/2	.79167
1 7/8	.15625	4 7/8	.40625	9 3/4	.81250
2	.16666	5	.41667	10	.83333
2 1/8	.17708	5 1/8	.42708	10 1/4	.85417
2 1/4	.18750	5 1/4	.43750	10 1/2	.87500
2 3/8	.19792	5 3/8	.44792	10 3/4	.89583
2 1/2	.20833	5 1/2	.45833	11	.91667
2 5/8	.21875	5 5/8	.46875	11 1/4	.93750
2 3/4	.22917	5 3/4	.47917	11 1/2	.95833
2 7/8	.23959	5 7/8	.48958	11 3/4	.97917
3	.25000	6	.50000	12	1.00000

Note: To change inches to decimals of a foot, divide by 12.

To change decimals of a foot to inches, multiply by 12.

CIRCUMFERENCES AND AREAS OF CIRCLES

Diameter, in Inches	Circumference	Area
1/64	.0491	.0002
1/32	.0982	.0008
1/16	.1964	.0031
3/32	.2945	.0069
1/8	.3927	.0123
5/32	.4909	.0192
3/16	.5890	.0276
7/32	.6872	.0376
1/4	.7854	.0491
9/32	.8836	.0621
5/16	.9817	.0767
11/32	1.0799	.0928
3/8	1.1781	.1105
13/32	1.2763	.1296
7/16	1.3745	.1503
15/32	1.4726	.1726
1/2	1.5708	.1964
17/32	1.6690	.2217
9/16	1.7672	.2485
19/32	1.8653	.2769
5/8	1.9635	.3068
21/32	2.0617	.3382
11/16	2.1598	.3712
23/32	2.2580	.4057
3/4	2.3562	.4418
25/32	2.4544	.4794
13/16	2.5525	.5185
27/32	2.6507	.5591
7/8	2.7489	.6013
29/32	2.8471	.6450
15/16	2.9452	.6903
31/32	3.0434	.7371
1	3.1416	.7854
1 1/16	3.3379	.8866
1 1/8	3.5343	.9940
1 3/16	3.7306	1.1075
1 1/4	3.9270	1.2272
1 5/16	4.1233	1.3530
1 3/8	4.3197	1.4849
1 7/16	4.5160	1.6230
1 1/2	4.7120	1.7671
1 9/16	4.9087	1.9175
1 5/8	5.1051	2.0739
1 11/16	5.3014	2.2365
1 3/4	5.4978	2.4053
1 13/16	5.6941	2.5802
1 7/8	5.8905	2.7612
1 15/16	6.0868	2.9483
2	6.2832	3.1416
2 1/16	6.4795	3.3410
2 1/8	6.6759	3.5466
2 3/16	6.8722	3.7583
2 1/4	7.0686	3.9761

Note: If the exact circumference or area wanted is not given in the table, it may be found by the following formulas: The *circumference* of a circle equals the diameter multiplied by 3.1416. The *area* of a circle equals the square of the diameter multiplied by .7854.

CIRCUMFERENCES AND AREAS (Cont'd)

Diameter, in Inches	Circumference	Area
2 5/16	7.2649	4.2000
2 3/8	7.4613	4.4301
2 7/16	7.6576	4.6664
2 1/2	7.8540	4.9087
2 9/16	8.0503	5.1572
2 5/8	8.2467	5.4119
2 11/16	8.4430	5.6727
2 3/4	8.6394	5.9396
2 13/16	8.8357	6.2126
2 7/8	9.0321	6.4918
2 15/16	9.2284	6.7771
3	9.4248	7.0686
3 1/16	9.6211	7.3662
3 1/8	9.8175	7.6699
3 3/16	10.0138	7.9798
3 1/4	10.2102	8.2958
3 5/16	10.4065	8.6179
3 3/8	10.6029	8.9462
3 7/16	10.7992	9.2806
3 1/2	10.9956	9.6211
3 9/16	11.1919	9.9678
3 5/8	11.3883	10.321
3 11/16	11.5846	10.680
3 3/4	11.7810	11.045
3 13/16	11.9773	11.416
3 7/8	12.1737	11.793
3 15/16	12.3700	12.177
4	12.5664	12.566
4 1/16	12.7627	12.962
4 1/8	12.9591	13.364
4 3/16	13.1554	13.772
4 1/4	13.3518	14.186
4 5/16	13.5481	14.607
4 3/8	13.7445	15.033

Area	Circumference	Diameter, in Inches
15.466	13.9408	4 7/16
15.904	14.1372	4 1/2
16.349	14.3335	4 9/16
16.800	14.5299	4 5/8
17.257	14.7262	4 11/16
17.721	14.9226	4 3/4
18.190	15.1189	4 13/16
18.665	15.3153	4 7/8
19.147	15.5116	4 15/16
19.635	15.7080	5
20.129	15.9043	5 1/16
20.629	16.1007	5 1/8
21.135	16.2970	5 3/16
21.648	16.4934	5 1/4
22.166	16.6897	5 5/16
22.691	16.8861	5 3/8
23.221	17.0824	5 7/16
23.758	17.2788	5 1/2
24.301	17.4751	5 9/16
24.850	17.6715	5 5/8
25.406	17.8678	5 11/16
25.967	18.0642	5 3/4
26.535	18.2605	5 13/16
27.109	18.4569	5 7/8
27.688	18.6532	5 15/16
28.274	18.8496	6
29.465	19.2423	6 1/8
30.680	19.6350	6 1/4
31.919	20.0277	6 3/8
33.183	20.4204	6 1/2
34.472	20.8131	6 5/8
35.785	21.2058	6 3/4
37.122	21.5984	6 7/8

CIRCUMFERENCES AND AREAS (Cont'd)

Diameter, in Inches	Circumference	Area	Diameter, in Inches	Circumference	Area
7	21.9911	38.485		34.9502	97.205
1/8	22.3838	39.871	1/8	35.3429	99.402
1/4	22.7765	41.282	1/4	35.7356	101.62
3/8	23.1692	42.718	3/8	36.1283	103.87
1/2	23.5619	44.179	1/2	36.5210	106.14
5/8	23.9546	45.664	5/8	36.9137	108.43
3/4	24.3473	47.173	3/4	37.3064	110.75
7/8	24.7400	48.707	7/8	37.6991	113.10
8	25.1327	50.265	12	38.4845	117.86
1/8	25.5254	51.849	1/4	39.2699	122.72
1/4	25.9181	53.456	1/2	40.0553	127.68
3/8	26.3108	55.088	3/4	40.8407	132.73
1/2	26.7035	56.745	13	41.6261	137.89
5/8	27.0962	58.426	1/4	42.4115	143.14
3/4	27.4889	60.132	1/2	43.1969	148.49
7/8	27.8816	61.862	3/4	43.9823	153.94
9	28.2743	63.617	14	44.7677	159.48
1/8	28.6670	65.397	1/4	45.5531	165.13
1/4	29.0597	67.201	1/2	46.3385	170.87
3/8	29.4524	69.029	3/4	47.1239	176.71
1/2	29.8451	70.882	15	47.9093	182.65
5/8	30.2378	72.760	1/4	48.6947	188.69
3/4	30.6305	74.662	1/2	49.4801	194.83
7/8	31.0232	76.589	3/4	50.2655	201.06
10	31.4159	78.540	16	51.0509	207.39
1/8	31.8086	80.516	1/4	51.8363	213.82
1/4	32.2013	82.516	1/2	52.6217	220.35
3/8	32.5940	84.541	3/4	53.4071	226.98
1/2	32.9867	86.590	17	54.1925	233.71
5/8	33.3794	88.664	1/4	54.9779	240.53
3/4	33.7721	90.763	1/2	55.7633	247.45
7/8	34.1648	92.886	3/4	56.5487	254.47
11	34.5575	95.033	18	57.3341	261.59
			1/4		

CIRCUMFERENCES AND AREAS

Diameter, in Inches	Circumference	Area	Diameter, in Inches	Circumference	Area
18½	58.1195	268.80	27¼	85.609	583.21
18¾	58.9049	276.12	27½	86.394	593.96
19	59.6903	283.53	27¾	87.179	604.81
19¼	60.4757	291.04	28	87.965	615.75
19½	61.2611	298.65	28¼	88.750	626.80
19¾	62.0465	306.35	28½	89.536	637.94
20	62.8319	314.14	28¾	90.321	649.18
20¼	63.6173	322.06	29	91.106	660.52
20½	64.4026	330.06	29¼	91.892	671.96
20¾	65.1880	338.16	29½	92.677	683.49
21	65.9734	346.36	29¾	93.463	695.13
21¼	66.7588	354.66	30	94.248	706.86
21½	67.5442	363.05	30¼	95.033	716.69
21¾	68.3296	371.54	30½	95.819	730.62
22	69.1150	380.13	30¾	96.604	742.64
22¼	69.9004	388.82	31	97.390	754.77
22½	70.6858	397.61	31¼	98.175	766.99
22¾	71.4712	406.49	31½	98.960	779.31
23	72.2566	415.48	31¾	99.746	791.73
23¼	73.0420	424.56	32	100.531	804.25
23½	73.8274	433.74	32¼	101.317	816.86
23¾	74.6128	443.01	32½	102.102	829.58
24	75.3982	452.39	32¾	102.887	842.39
24¼	76.1836	461.86	33	103.673	855.30
24½	76.9690	471.44	33¼	104.458	868.31
24¾	77.7544	481.11	33½	105.244	881.41
25	78.540	490.87	33¾	106.029	894.62
25¼	79.325	500.74	34	106.814	907.92
25½	80.111	510.71	34¼	107.600	921.32
25¾	80.896	520.77	34½	108.385	934.82
26	81.682	530.93	34¾	109.171	948.42
26¼	82.467	541.19	35	109.956	962.11
26½	83.252	551.55	35¼	110.741	975.91
26¾	84.038	562.00	35½	111.527	989.80
27	84.823	572.56	35¾	112.312	1003.79

CIRCUMFERENCES AND AREAS (Cont'd)

Diameter, in Inches	Circumference	Area	Diameter, in Inches	Circumference	Area
36	113.098	1017.88	43¼	135.874	1469.14
36¼	113.883	1032.06	43½	136.660	1486.17
36½	114.668	1046.35	43¾	137.445	1503.30
36¾	115.454	1060.73	44	138.230	1520.53
37	116.239	1075.21	44¼	139.016	1537.86
37¼	117.025	1089.79	44½	139.801	1555.29
37½	117.810	1104.47	44¾	140.587	1572.81
37¾	118.595	1119.24	45	141.372	1590.43
38	119.381	1134.12	45¼	142.157	1608.16
38¼	120.166	1149.09	45½	142.943	1625.97
38½	120.952	1164.16	45¾	143.728	1643.89
38¾	121.737	1179.33	46	144.514	1661.91
39	122.522	1194.59	46¼	145.299	1680.02
39¼	123.308	1209.96	46½	146.084	1698.23
39½	124.093	1225.42	46¾	146.870	1716.54
39¾	124.879	1240.98	47	147.655	1734.95
40	125.664	1256.64	47¼	148.441	1753.45
40¼	126.449	1272.40	47½	149.226	1772.06
40½	127.235	1288.25	47¾	150.011	1790.76
40¾	128.020	1304.21	48	150.797	1809.56
41	128.806	1320.26	48¼	151.582	1828.46
41¼	129.591	1336.41	48½	152.368	1847.46
41½	130.376	1352.66	48¾	153.153	1866.55
41¾	131.162	1369.00	49	153.938	1885.75
42	131.947	1385.45	49¼	154.724	1905.04
42¼	132.733	1401.99	49½	155.509	1924.43
42½	133.518	1418.63	49¾	156.295	1943.91
42¾	134.303	1435.37	50	157.080	1963.50
43	135.089	1452.20			

SQUARES, CUBES, AND SQUARE AND CUBE ROOTS

No.	Square	Cube	Square Root	Cube Root
1	1	1	1.000	1.000
2	4	8	1.414	1.260
3	9	27	1.732	1.442
4	16	64	2.000	1.587
5	25	125	2.236	1.710
6	36	216	2.449	1.817
7	49	343	2.646	1.913
8	64	512	2.828	2.000
9	81	729	3.000	2.080
10	100	1,000	3.162	2.154
11	121	1,331	3.317	2.224
12	144	1,728	3.464	2.289
13	169	2,197	3.606	2.351
14	196	2,744	3.742	2.410
15	225	3,375	3.873	2.466
16	256	4,096	4.000	2.520
17	289	4,913	4.123	2.571
18	324	5,832	4.243	2.621
19	361	6,859	4.359	2.668
20	400	8,000	4.472	2.714
21	441	9,261	4.583	2.759
22	484	10,648	4.690	2.802
23	529	12,167	4.796	2.844
24	576	13,824	4.899	2.884
25	625	15,625	5.000	2.924
26	676	17,576	5.099	2.962
27	729	19,683	5.196	3.000
28	784	21,952	5.292	3.037
29	841	24,389	5.385	3.072
30	900	27,000	5.477	3.107
31	961	29,791	5.568	3.141
32	1,024	32,768	5.657	3.175
33	1,089	35,937	5.745	3.208
34	1,156	39,304	5.831	3.240
35	1,225	42,875	5.916	3.271

SQUARES, CUBES, AND SQUARE AND CUBE ROOTS (Cont'd)

No.	Square	Cube	Square Root	Cube Root
36	1,296	46,656	6.000	3.302
37	1,369	50,653	6.083	3.332
38	1,444	54,872	6.164	3.362
39	1,521	59,319	6.245	3.391
40	1,600	64,000	6.325	3.420
41	1,681	68,921	6.403	3.448
42	1,764	74,088	6.481	3.476
43	1,849	79,507	6.557	3.503
44	1,936	85,184	6.633	3.530
45	2,025	91,125	6.708	3.557
46	2,116	97,336	6.782	3.583
47	2,209	103,823	6.856	3.609
48	2,304	110,592	6.928	3.634
49	2,401	117,649	7.000	3.659
50	2,500	125,000	7.071	3.684
51	2,601	132,651	7.141	3.708
52	2,704	140,608	7.211	3.733
53	2,809	148,877	7.280	3.756
54	2,916	157,464	7.348	3.780
55	3,025	166,375	7.416	3.803
56	3,136	175,616	7.483	3.826
57	3,249	185,193	7.550	3.849
58	3,364	195,112	7.616	3.871
59	3,481	205,379	7.681	3.893
60	3,600	216,000	7.746	3.915
61	3,721	226,981	7.810	3.936
62	3,844	238,328	7.874	3.958
63	3,969	250,047	7.937	3.979
64	4,096	262,144	8.000	4.000
65	4,225	274,625	8.062	4.021
66	4,356	287,496	8.124	4.041
67	4,489	300,763	8.185	4.062
68	4,624	314,432	8.264	4.082
69	4,761	328,509	8.307	4.102
70	4,900	343,000	8.367	4.121

SQUARES, CUBES, AND SQUARE AND CUBE ROOTS (Cont'd)

No.	Square	Cube	Square Root	Cube Root
71	5,041	357,911	8.426	4.141
72	5,184	373,248	8.485	4.160
73	5,329	389,017	8.544	4.179
74	5,476	405,224	8.602	4.198
75	5,625	421,875	8.660	4.217
76	5,776	438,976	8.718	4.236
77	5,929	456,533	8.775	4.254
78	6,084	474,552	8.832	4.273
79	6,241	493,039	8.888	4.291
80	6,400	512,000	8.944	4.309
81	6,561	531,441	9.000	4.327
82	6,724	551,368	9.055	4.344
83	6,889	571,787	9.110	4.362
84	7,056	592,704	9.165	4.380
85	7,225	614,125	9.220	4.397
86	7,396	636,056	9.274	4.414
87	7,569	658,503	9.327	4.431
88	7,744	681,472	9.381	4.448
89	7,921	704,969	9.434	4.465
90	8,100	729,000	9.487	4.481
91	8,281	753,571	9.539	4.498
92	8,464	778,688	9.592	4.514
93	8,649	804,357	9.644	4.531
94	8,836	830,584	9.695	4.547
95	9,025	857,375	9.747	4.563
96	9,216	884,736	9.798	4.579
97	9,409	912,673	9.849	4.595
98	9,604	941,192	9.899	4.610
99	9,801	970,299	9.950	4.626
100	10,000	1,000,000	10.000	4.642

SQUARE ROOT OF FRACTIONS

Fraction	Square Root
1/8	.3535
1/4	.5000
3/8	.6124
1/2	.7071
5/8	.7906
3/4	.8660
7/8	.9354

CUBE ROOT OF FRACTIONS

Fraction	Cube Root
1/8	.5000
1/4	.6300
3/8	.7211
1/2	.7937
5/8	.8550
3/4	.9086
7/8	.9565

TRIGONOMETRY TABLE

Deg.	Min.	Sine	Cosine	Tangent	Cotangent	Secant	Cosecant		
0	00	.00000	1.00000	.00000	Infinite	1.0000	Infinite	90	
1		.01745	.99985	.01745	57.290	1.0001	57.299	89	
1	30	.02618	.99966	.02618	38.188	1.0003	38.201	88	30
2		.03490	.99939	.03492	28.636	1.0006	28.654	88	
2	30	.04362	.99905	.04366	22.904	1.0009	22.925	87	30
3		.05234	.99863	.05241	19.081	1.0014	19.107	87	
3	30	.06105	.99813	.06116	16.350	1.0019	16.380	86	30
4		.06976	.99756	.06993	14.301	1.0024	14.335	86	
4	30	.07846	.99692	.07870	12.706	1.0031	12.745	85	30
5		.08715	.99619	.08749	11.430	1.0038	11.474	85	
5	30	.09584	.99540	.09629	10.385	1.0046	10.433	84	30
6		.10453	.99452	.10510	9.5144	1.0055	9.5668	84	
6	30	.11320	.99357	.11393	8.7769	1.0065	8.8337	83	30
7		.12187	.99255	.12278	8.1443	1.0075	8.2055	83	
7	30	.13053	.99144	.13165	7.5957	1.0086	7.6613	82	30
8		.13917	.99027	.14054	7.1154	1.0098	7.1853	82	
8	30	.14781	.98901	.14945	6.6911	1.0111	6.7655	81	30
9		.15643	.98769	.15838	6.3137	1.0125	6.3924	81	
9	30	.16505	.98628	.16734	5.9758	1.0139	6.0538	80	30
		Cosine	Sine	Cotangent	Tangent	Cosecant	Secant	Deg.	Min.

TRIGONOMETRY TABLE (Cont'd)

Deg.	Min.	Sine	Cosine	Tangent	Cotangent	Secant	Cosecant		
10		.17365	.98481	.17633	5.6713	1.0154	5.7588	80	
10	30	.18223	.98325	.18534	5.3955	1.0170	5.4874	79	30
11		.19081	.98163	.19438	5.1445	1.0187	5.2408	79	
11	30	.19937	.97972	.20345	4.9151	1.0205	5.0158	78	30
12		.20791	.97815	.21256	4.7046	1.0223	4.8097	78	
12	30	.21644	.97630	.22169	4.5170	1.0243	4.6201	77	30
13		.22495	.97437	.23087	4.3315	1.0263	4.4454	77	
13	30	.23344	.97237	.24008	4.1653	1.0284	4.2836	76	30
14		.24192	.97029	.24933	4.0108	1.0306	4.1336	76	
14	30	.25038	.96815	.25862	3.8667	1.0329	3.9939	75	30
15		.25882	.96592	.26795	3.7320	1.0353	3.8637	75	
15	30	.26724	.96363	.27732	3.6059	1.0377	3.7420	74	30
16		.27564	.96126	.28674	3.4874	1.0403	3.6279	74	
16	30	.28401	.95882	.29621	3.3759	1.0429	3.5209	73	30
17		.29237	.95630	.30573	3.2708	1.0457	3.4203	73	
17	30	.30070	.95372	.31530	3.1716	1.0485	3.3255	72	30
18		.30902	.95106	.32492	3.0777	1.0515	3.2361	72	
18	30	.31730	.94832	.33459	2.9887	1.0545	3.1515	71	30
		Cosine	Sine	Cotangent	Tangent	Cosecant	Secant	Deg.	Min.

TRIGONOMETRY TABLE (Cont'd)

Deg.	Min.	Sine	Cosine	Tangent	Cotangent	Secant	Cosecant		
19		.32557	.94552	.34433	2.9042	1.0576	3.0715	71	
19	30	.33381	.94264	.35412	2.8239	1.0608	2.9957	70	30
20		.34202	.93969	.36397	2.7475	1.0642	2.9238	70	
20	30	.35031	.93667	.37388	2.6746	1.0676	2.8554	69	30
21		.35837	.93358	.38386	2.6051	1.0711	2.7904	69	
21	30	.36650	.93042	.39391	2.5386	1.0748	2.7285	68	30
22		.37461	.92718	.40403	2.4751	1.0785	2.6695	68	
22	30	.38268	.92388	.41421	2.4142	1.0824	2.6131	67	30
23		.39073	.92050	.42447	2.3558	1.0864	2.5593	67	
23	30	.39875	.91706	.43481	2.2998	1.0904	2.5078	66	30
24		.40674	.91354	.44523	2.2460	1.0946	2.4586	66	
24	30	.41469	.90996	.45573	2.1943	1.0989	2.4114	65	30
25		.42262	.90631	.46631	2.1445	1.1034	2.3662	65	
25	30	.43051	.90258	.47697	2.0965	1.1079	2.3228	64	30
26		.43837	.89879	.48773	2.0503	1.1126	2.2812	64	
26	30	.44620	.89493	.49858	2.0057	1.1174	2.2411	63	30
27		.45399	.89101	.50952	1.9626	1.1223	2.2027	63	
27	30	.46175	.88701	.52057	1.9210	1.1274	2.1657	62	30
		Cosine	Sine	Cotangent	Tangent	Cosecant	Secant	Deg.	Min.

TRIGONOMETRY TABLE (Cont'd)

Deg.	Min.	Sine	Cosine	Tangent	Cotangent	Secant	Cosecant		
28		.46947	.88295	.53171	1.8807	1.1326	2.1300	62	
28	30	.47716	.87882	.54295	1.8418	1.1379	2.0957	61	30
29		.48481	.87462	.55431	1.8040	1.1433	2.0627	61	
29	30	.49242	.87035	.56577	1.7675	1.1489	2.0308	60	30
30		.50000	.86603	.57735	1.7320	1.1547	2.0000	60	
30	30	.50754	.86163	.58904	1.6977	1.1606	1.9703	59	30
31		.51504	.85717	.60086	1.6643	1.1666	1.9416	59	
31	30	.52250	.85264	.61280	1.6318	1.1728	1.9139	58	30
32		.52992	.84805	.62487	1.6003	1.1792	1.8871	58	
32	30	.53730	.84339	.63707	1.5697	1.1857	1.8611	57	30
33		.54464	.83867	.64941	1.5399	1.1924	1.8361	57	
33	30	.55191	.83388	.66188	1.5108	1.1992	1.8118	56	30
34		.55919	.82904	.67451	1.4826	1.2062	1.7883	56	
34	30	.56641	.82413	.68728	1.4550	1.2134	1.7655	55	30
35		.57358	.81915	.70021	1.4281	1.2208	1.7434	55	
35	30	.58070	.81411	.71329	1.4019	1.2283	1.7220	54	30
36		.58778	.80902	.72654	1.3764	1.2361	1.7013	54	
36	30	.59482	.80386	.73996	1.3514	1.2442	1.6812	53	30
		Cosine	Sine	Cotangent	Tangent	Cosecant	Secant	Deg.	Min.

TRIGONOMETRY TABLE (Cont'd)

Deg.	Min.	Sine	Cosine	Tangent	Cotangent	Secant	Cosecant		
37		.60181	.79863	.75355	1.3270	1.2521	1.6616	53	
37	30	.60876	.79335	.76733	1.3032	1.2605	1.6427	52	
38		.61566	.78801	.78128	1.2799	1.2690	1.6243	52	30
38	30	.62251	.78261	.79543	1.2572	1.2778	1.6064	51	30
39		.62932	.77715	.80978	1.2349	1.2867	1.5890	51	
39	30	.63608	.77162	.82434	1.2131	1.2960	1.5721	50	30
40		.64279	.76604	.83910	1.1917	1.3054	1.5557	50	
40	30	.64945	.76041	.85408	1.1708	1.3151	1.5398	49	30
41		.65606	.75471	.86929	1.1504	1.3250	1.5242	49	
41	30	.66262	.74895	.88472	1.1303	1.3352	1.5092	48	30
42		.66913	.74314	.90040	1.1106	1.3456	1.4945	48	
42	30	.67559	.73728	.91633	1.0913	1.3563	1.4802	47	30
43		.68200	.73135	.93251	1.0724	1.3673	1.4663	47	
43	30	.68835	.72357	.94896	1.0538	1.3786	1.4527	46	30
44		.69466	.71934	.96569	1.0355	1.3902	1.4395	46	
44	30	.70091	.71325	.98270	1.0176	1.4020	1.4267	45	30
45		.70711	.70711	1.00000	1.0000	1.4142	1.4142	45	
		Cosine	Sine	Cotangent	Tangent	Cosecant	Secant	Deg.	Min.

NOTES

NOTES